NATIONAL ARCHAEOLOGICAL MUSEUM

COLLECTION OF SCULPTURE

ARCHAEOLOGICAL GUIDES OF THE
GEN. DIRECTION OF ANTIQUITIES AND RESTORATION

1. Carl Blegen - Marion Rawson, Τὸ Ἀνάκτορον τοῦ Νέστορος (μετάφρασις Γ. Α. Παπαθανασοπούλου). Ἀθῆναι, 1964 (2α ἔκδοσις) (ἐξηντλήθη).

2. Ἀγνῆς Σακελλαρίου - Γ. Παπαθανασοπούλου, Ἐθνικὸν Ἀρχαιολογικὸν Μουσεῖον. Α΄. Προϊστορικαὶ Συλλογαί. Σύντομος Ὁδηγός. Ἀθῆναι, 1964 (ἀνατύπωσις 1973).

3. N. Platon, A Guide to the Archaeological Museum of Heraclion. Athens, 1964.

4. N. Platon, Führer durch das Archäologische Museum von Heraklion. Athen, 1964.

5. Agnes Sakellariou - G. A. Papathanasopoulos, National Archaeological Museum. I. Prehistoric Collections. A Brief Guide (translated into English by Helen Wace, Elizabeth Wace - French and Ariadne Koumari - Sandorf). Athens, 1964 (out of press).

7. A Concise Guide to the Acropolis Museum (translated by Helen Wace and Elizabeth Wace - French). Athens, 1965 (reprinted 1974).

8. Ἀμερικανικῆς Σχολῆς Κλασσικῶν Σπουδῶν. Ὁδηγὸς τῆς Ἀρχαίας Ἀγορᾶς τῶν Ἀθηνῶν (μετάφρασις Σ. Πλάτωνος). Ἀθῆναι, 1965 (ἀνατύπωσις 1974).

9. Agnès Sakellariou - G. A. Papathanassopoulos. Musée Archéologique National. A΄. Collections Préhistoriques. Guide Sommaire. Athènes, 1965 (réimpression 1974).

10. Guide Sommaire du Musée de l'Acropole. Athènes, 1966 (épuisé).

11. Agnes Sakellariou - G. A. Papathanassopoulos, Archäologiches Nationalmuseum. I. Vorgeschichtliche Sammlungen. Kurzführer (übersetzt von Maria Hermann). Athen, 1966 (Nachdruck 1974).

12. Kurzer Führer durch das Akropolis. Museum (übersetzt von Char. Neumann). Athen, 1967 (Nachdruck 1974).

13. Σέμνης Καρούζου, Ἐθνικὸν Ἀρχαιολογικὸν Μουσεῖον. Συλλογὴ Γλυπτῶν. Περιγραφικὸς Κατάλογος. Ἀθῆναι, 1967.

14. S. Karouzou, Musée Archéologique National. Collection des Sculptures. Catalogue descriptif (traduit par X. Lefcoparides). Athènes, 1968.

15. S. Karouzou, National Archaeological Museum. Collection of Sculpture. A Catalogue (translated by Helen Wace). Athens, 1968 (reprinted 1974).

16. Guida breve del Museo dell'Acropoli (trad. di Dina Peppas-Delmusu). Atene, 1967.

DEDICATED
AS A MEMORIAL
TO
THE DIRECTOR 1942 - 1964
WHO INSPIRED THE REBIRTH OF THE NATIONAL MUSEUM
AFTER THE SECOND WORLD WAR

GUIDES: No 15

The Catalogue was translated by Mrs Helen Wace.

The cover design is by the artist of the National Museum, Mr. Pan. Sarafianos.

S. KAROUZOU

NATIONAL ARCHAEOLOGICAL MUSEUM

COLLECTION OF SCULPTURE

A CATALOGUE

REPRINTED 1974

GENERAL DIRECTION OF ANTIQUITIES AND RESTORATION

ATHENS, 1968

FOREWORD

The publication of a catalogue of the sculptures of the National Museum was put in hand after the exhibition, in the 26 halls of the old building as well as in the interior court, was completed.

In view of the persistent demand for a guide, it was thought necessary to omit bibliography from this catalogue, the first to be published after the war, as its preparation would have caused considerable delay in the publication.

The description of each work is followed by the place where it was found and the year, its measurements and its date. In cases where the year is not mentioned, this means either that it is not known when the work was found, or that the date has not been verified. The inventory of the sculptures in the National Museum proved, in most cases, to be the most trustworthy source for this kind of information. The descriptions of the sculptures in the first galleries are shorter because, at the beginning, a shorter and more concise guide was planned. A description of sculptures of the Graeco-Roman period, and especially of the excellent collection of portraits, is not included, because the exhibition of these works has not been completed.

Naturally there may be some errors and omissions in the description of such a vast number of sculptures; in matters concerning dates and interpretation, opinions expressed here may on occasion differ from prevailing views; this, however, has not been done without some reflection; it is the result of familiarity with the works concerned.

I should like to extend my thanks to the General Direction of Antiquities and Restoration of the Ministry of the Prime Minister for their kindness in including this book in the series of their dublications.

Sincere and warm thanks go to Mrs. Athina Kaloyeropoulou, Head of the Office of Publications of the General Direction of Antiquities for her invaluable and unceasing help
toward the best possible presentation of the catalogue, as well
as to Professor Andreas Xyngopoulos for the care he has taken
over the illustrations.

Of the members of the staff of the Office of Publications,
who helped devotedly in the preparation of the publication, I
wish to thank Mrs. Loula Kypraiou, Miss Sonia Kaloyeropoulou
and Miss Ketty Ftyara.

I also wish to extend my warm thanks to Mrs Helen
Wace for her excellent translation into English of the text of
this catalogue. The English translation is based on a version
of the Greek text a little earlier than that published. Some
additions have also been made by the author to the English
text. A list of c o r r i g e n d a is appended which attempts
to reconcile the English and Greek published texts.

S. K.

A CONCISE HISTORY OF THE NATIONAL MUSEUM

On February 6th, 1835 according to a decision of the Holy Synod, it was ordered that the Altar, as well as « every other ecclesiastical object be removed from the Theseum temple », which had, until then, been used as a Christian church.

Shortly before this, it had been stipulated by a Royal Decree dated November 13, 1834, that the Theseum should become the « Central Archaeological Museum ». Its core would be the sculptures collected by the Ephor of Antiquities Kyriakos Pittakis in 1833 and kept at the Church of the Great Panaghia. He had left on the Acropolis the sculptures found there.

That in the Theseum was not, however, the first archaeological collection to be formed after independence was won [1]. In March 1829, during Kapodistria's rule, the first Archaeological Museum had been established in Aegina, then the temporary capital, and Andreas Moustoxidis from Corfu was the Ephor (Inspector). A catalogue of its contents (up to July 1832) had been prepared by the Archimandrite Leontios Kambanis. Later the painter Athanassios Iatridis was appointed Superintendent of the Museum.

When the seat of the General Ephor Ludwig Ross was transferred to Athens, it was natural that the main centre for the collection of antiquities should be established here, in the permanent capital of the country. By 1836, the Theseum was already full and the Ephor Pittakis was obliged to keep sculptures in the Library of Had-

---

1. Ancient sculptures had been brought to safety in the Monastery of Loukou (Kynouria, Peloponnese) from the very beginning of the 19th century. The sculptures were reproduced in drawings in the excellent monumental volume: Expédition Scientifique de Morée (Paris 1839), vol. III, pl. 88 - 91.

rian as well. It was to here that in September 1837 all the most important works were transferred from the Aegina Museum, apart from some of secondary value, which were left there. From 1841 onwards the number of antiquities found and put in store increased so much that it became necessary to place them even in the offices of the General Ephorate and after 1843 in the Tower of the Winds as well. It was to these public collections, that the Archaeological Society (which had been founded in 1837) gave all the works that it had acquired either by purchase or from excavations which had been carried out on its initiative and with its financial assistance.

In 1858 - 1859 the Archaeological Society established its own first temporary Museum in a room in the University. Thereafter, under the care of its Secretary, Stefanos Koumanoudis, this Museum became increasingly richer through excavations as well as through the purchase of antiquities. Then, in 1865 the Government provided six rooms in the Varvakeion where these treasures could be housed; here, on certain days of the week, admission was open to the public.

However, the need for a large public Museum had become generally felt. Around 1835, Leo von Klenze had made architectural designs for a Central Museum, — « Pantechneion » (for all Arts) as he called it, a building with three floors and a large rotunda on the ground floor. Its façade recalled another of his buildings, the Old Pinakotheke in Munich. It would have looked imposing and stately, a little withdrawn from the outside.

More adapted to the Greek climate and light were the designs by an artist of the northern romantic school, Ludwig Lange. painter and architect, and a pupil of Rotmann; his designs were executed though not without alterations.

An important event took place in 1866. Eleni Tositsa

donated a large plot of land and the construction of the building, based on Lange's drawings, began. A Greek from Petrograd, the Cretan Demetrios Bernardakis, one of the great benefactors of the nation, offered the substantial sum of 250,000 drachmae for the construction of the building. In 1874 the Greek government offered financial assistance which made possible the completion of the west wing of the building which was the only part already under construction. To this wing were transferred, that same year, the antiquities from the Theseum, the Varvakeion and the Library of Hadrian.

In 1881 a large number of sculptures was scattered in disorder all over the floor of the finished west wing. The descriptive catalogue of Sybel contained 2682 sculptures[1]. In the same year, in the more concise catalogue by Milchhöfer there is also a drawing of this side of the building without the Propylaia[2]. Important sculptures were still kept in the Theseum and outside it. In the open and on the southeast side of the temple, stood the colossal Nike of Megara. In the National Museum, where this Nike has since been transferred, there will never be found a place as appropriate as that, where it reminded one of the statue's ancient splendour, surrounded, as it had once been, by air and light.

Some public collections still remained in the Ministry of Education, in the Kerameikos (Holy Trinity Church), on the Acropolis, in the Library of Hadrian and the General Ephorate. The collection of the Archaeological Society was kept in the Varvakeion and in the Polytechnic School and included Schliemann's precious finds from Mycenae as well as other antiquities of the Mycenean period. Here too was kept the collection of Egyptian antiquities, donated by Ioannis Demetriou from Lemnos.

1. L. Sybel, Skulpturen zu Athen (Marburg 1881).
2. A. Milchhöfer, Die Museen Athens (Athen 1881).

It is worth noting that Sybel speaks about a « Central » Museum while Milchhöfer already calls it National. It seems that the change of name was then being discussed and was soon officially ratified by Charilaos Tricoupis. The warm attachment of this great and progressive politician to the idea of Museums is well known (he also made donations of ancient works of art). It was on his personal initiative that there was issued the Royal Decree of April 19th, 1881, which ordered that the name of the Central Museum be changed to « National Archaeological Museum ».

In 1889 the whole building was completed. The east wing, the central hall and the main façade as designed by Lange were modified by Ernst Ziller, a gifted, younger architect, known for his many artistic achievements in Greece and also for his archaeological research.

An important enrichment of the National Museum took place in 1891,.when all the antiquities owned by the Archaeological Society were transferred to it. The Archaeological Society ceased to have its own Museum and its valuable contribution to the Museum's development was over. The installation of the sculptures and the exhibition of the other works of art was effected at a quicker pace by Panaghiotis Kavvadias, who had already prepared a guide of the sculptures (first in 1887, then in 1890-1892). Christos Tsountas, with his deep knowledge and scientific mind, began to prepare a valuable inventory of the Myc. collection of the Museum; Pan. Kastriotis took charge of, completed and brought up to date in a most exemplary manner, the inventory of the sculptures; he also had a catalogue printed[1].

The two catalogues of Valerios Stais, the one of the prehistoric collection and the other of the sculptures and

---

1. Panaghiotis Kastriotis, Sculptures of the National Museum. Athens 1908.

the bronzes in the Museum, were prepared in French[1].
Around 1925, the display of every kind of ancient work
of art had become so overcrowded that some of the galleries
looked like storerooms. A generous and long-term financial contribution from the Government made possible the
extension which had become absolutely necessary. The
beautiful apsidal hall, which was in the centre of the east
wing and which sheltered the Museum's unique collection
of bronzes was demolished and the building of the new
extension began. This was done by sacrificing the big yard
which lay behind the old building. Small but pleasant,
the houses of the guards and the technicians used to give
it life and the tall pine trees reminded one of the serenity
of the Attica landscape. (The rear court of the Polytechnic
School ceased to exist at about the same time and the back
view of the two buildings, which had been so well studied
and so harmoniously linked together, was lost).

It was unfortunate that the drawings of the new extension, clinging as they did to an old-fashioned classicism in an attempt to be in keeping with the style of the
old building, resulted in giving the building a conventional look; the façade is graceless and cold. In 1939, the
building was ready; before, however, any moving of the
antiquities had begun, the second world war broke out
and in 1940 the Greek-Italian war followed.

Immediately after that morning of October 28th, when
the sirens announced the outbreak of the Greek-Italian
war, the treasures of the Museum were lifted off their bases, pulled off the walls and buried. It took Greek archaeologists six months to complete this most depressing task
(exactly as long as the Greek resistance in the Albanian

---

1. V. Staïs, La Collection Mycénienne du Musée National. Athens.
(1st edition 1908. 2nd edition 1915). V. Staïs. Marbres et Bronzes
du Musée National. Athens (1st edition 1907. 2nd edition 1910).

mountains lasted). A few foreign archaeologists kindly offered to assist in putting the vases into crates; their contribution was most helpful. All those who lived through the heart-rending experience of seeing hall after hall deserted, emptied of their sacred contents, will never forget it.

The galleries of the National Museum took their present form gradually, in the years after the end of the war. Important structural alterations which took many years were carried out in the old building, underground-rooms were created and the court was made into a garden to serve for spiritual relaxation after the inevitable weariness of visiting the Museum.

At the same time while this construction was being carried out, a number of the most important archaic and classical works of art were temporarily exhibited in ten rooms. For quite a number of years, until the construction was completed, these provided an oasis for archaeologists and friends of archaeology, a school for young people and children who had grown up without ancient works of art.

Let us go back to the war years in order to follow up the curious history of the Museum. Almost the whole of the old building as well as part of the new wing, was divided into smaller rooms in order to shelter the various public services which the army of occupation had turned out of their own buildings. The State Orchestra was established in the central, the old Mycenean hall. The Post Office was established in a large part of the west wing, to the right of the entrance, and the departments of the Ministry of Welfare in the galleries of the upper floor of the new wing. Other smaller areas were used as air-raid shelters, as kitchens, as centres for the distribution of communal meals etc.

In the west wing of the old building, on the left of the entrance, as well as in the north wing, the colossal Kouros of Sounion and other statues were buried. The sepulchral monuments, the marble stelai, the statues were buried in several layers. This was possible because of the high embankment which had served as a base — and, up to a certain level, as foundation — for the old building. This was the temporary grave of a large number of sculptures; if no harm was caused to the marbles, in spite of all these moves, it is mainly due to the fact that Andreas Panaghiotakis, old, experienced and devoted sculptor of the Museum Staff was in charge of the team of workers, then and until the first years after the war.

The semi-underground rooms of the new building were most useful for the storage and burial of the most important sculptures, for the great number of vases and the small works of art (the latter were put into two hundred boxes) and especially for the precious collection of ancient bronzes. These rooms were covered, all through the war years, with a thick layer of dry sand, so that they were protected from air-raids; in the same way many sacks of sand covered the windows facing the court. Some sculptures had been transferred to secret shelters, outside the Museum, while all the gold and precious exhibits of the Mycenean room, as well as the precious objects of other periods, were put into safety in deep, strongly built underground shelters of a large state building.

The opening of the large number of boxes became possible, after the end of the war, only when the thick covering of sand was removed; then followed the checking of the objects against the lists made when they were packed away.

The work of uncovering the sculptures and opening the boxes lasted a number of years as the scientific and technical personnel of the Museum was limited in numbers and the work was complex and demanding. The task of putting together clay works of art that had become either unglued or broken while in the boxes was extremely difficult; this work was done in the special laboratory for vases. Another difficult task was the preservation and restoration of bronze objects. The cleaning and restoration of the bronze Youth from Antikythera took nine months of intensive work; this was done by the late Andreas Panaghiotakis, sculptor, the late John Bakoulis, head - technician and the then Director of the Museum.

Let the visitor, who enjoys the restored antiquities in the Museum galleries, think of the tremendous work put in by the artists of the Museum, the sculptors and painters; let the visitor think of the many technicians who worked with knowledge, faith and enthusiasm, so that these « long-suffering » works of art might be restored.

The most important of the reconstruction work in the old building was to remove the huge pile of earth in order to provide large spaces for storage, indispensable to every big Museum. The restoration of the wood-tied roof, which had been partially destroyed by machine gun fire from aircraft during the dark days of December 1944, was imperative. It had also to be modernized in order to exclude danger from fire.

The moving of a large number of sculptures, which had been laid in the open, or put in roughly constructed wooden huts in the court, or even in some dark remote corners of the old part of the Museum, became possible only when the big spaces for storage were completed, the so-called « new basements » (most of them looking onto Herakleiou Street).

The architect made important alterations which gave a pleasant look to the interior of the central entrance. Formerly dark, it became light by the addition of a glass roof and it also took on a monumental aspect when the pillars of the first two galleries were moved to the entrance.

The state's financial contribution, in the first years after the war, made it possible to remove the thick covering of sand and to create a temporary exhibition (the first three galleries were opened in 1946 when the Centenary of the French Archaeological School was celebrated). Later on, the construction works were financed by American Aid and then again the Greek Government made a permanent contribution for the new exhibition.

The fact that the modifications to the old building were carried out in a style faithful to the original creation of Lange and Ziller, that the old plan was kept yet related to the present needs for modernization (in those parts of the building that had to be reconstructed to ensure the preservation and best presentation of the contents) is due to the collaboration between Patroklos Karantinos, architect (Technical Department of the Ministry of Education) and Christos Karouzos, Director of the National Museum (1942 - 1964).

The chief aim in the new arrangement of the galleries was that the visitor should feel a warm and close communion with the works of art and that his heart be open to the art of all phases of Greek cultural activity. In this respect it has been of great help that the treasures of the National Museum are not housed in an old, dark palace as is generally the case in European capitals, but rather in a neo - classical building of the late 19th century, comparatively simple in design, without ornaments on the walls and without multicoloured marble dadoes.

However, the main contributors to the unforgettable impression made upon the visitor to the National Museum, the factor which differentiates it from other Museums, are the exhibits themselves and above all the sculptures. Most of them are originals, authentic Greek works, full of life and an innate conception of rhythm, which sprang from a « humanist » education; they are not copies like those which were mechanically carved during the years of the

2

Roman conquest when creative spirit had declined and the feeling for the organic rhythm of the human body had died away. In many European Museums, — which originally consisted mainly of older private post-Renaissance collections — the ancient sculptures, restored and « beautified », as was the fashion, give a false idea of Greek art. In the way this art is presented in the National Museum, without any glamourization, not only does it serve pure knowledge but it also broadens the intellect and intoxicates the spirit. The plaster and other restorations carried out in the previous century, at the beginning of the 20th century and more recently — after the last war — have been done with scientific accuracy, with discretion and with respect. The postwar exhibition was enriched, not only with new finds, the harvest of the Greek soil, but also with those objects which it was thought should be taken out of the basements, most of them unknown to research workers, forgotten or neglected.

No aesthetic theory, no *a priori* conception, dictated the selection and the exhibition of the works. This was based on a separate evaluation of each artistic object, each one considered as an individual work but also as part of an organic historical evolution. All that scientific research, critical analysis and an experienced eye can offer today were also employed : the description of the object, dating, work-shop, personality of the artist combined with the subject represented.

Finally, the placing of the works in the Museum was often dictated by the works themselves; sometimes they required space, sometimes isolation, sometimes the proximity of related works, sometimes a central position or a remote corner.

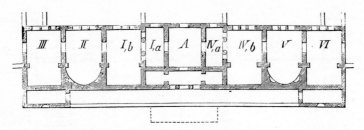

1. Ground - plan of the West Wing of the Museum in 1874

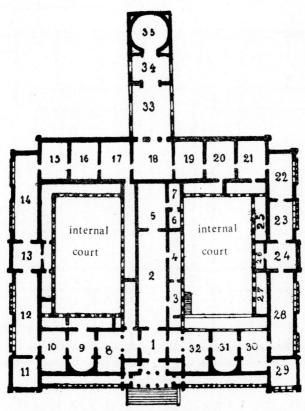

2. Ground - plan of the Museum Building in 1889

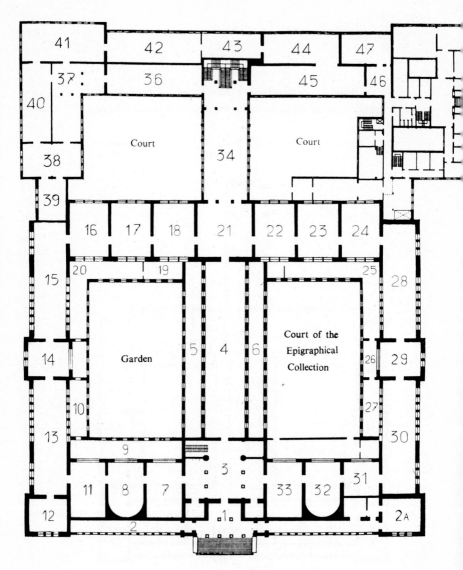

3. Ground-plan of the Main Floor
of the National Archaeological Museum, 1968

KEY TO PLAN 3

1 : Porch
2 : Northern Stoa
3 : Entrance Hall
4 : Mycenean Room
5 : Neolithic and Premycenean Room
6 : Cycladic Room
7 : 1st Room of Archaic Sculpture
8 : 2nd Room of Archaic Sculpture
9 - 10: Two small Rooms of Archaic Sculpture
11 : 3rd Room of Archaic Sculpture
12 : 4th Room of Archaic Sculpture
13 : Room of Aristodikos
14 : Late Archaic and early Classical Works
15 : Room of Poseidon
16 : 1st Room of Classical Grave Monuments
17 : Room of Classical Votive Sculpture
18 : 2nd Room of Classical Grave Monuments
19 - 20: Two small Rooms of Classical Sculpture
The Garden
21 : Room of the « Diadoumenos »
22 : Room of Epidaurus
23 : 1st Room of Grave Monuments of the 4th cent. B.C.
24 : 2nd Room of Grave Monuments of the 4th cent. B.C.
25 : Two Rooms of Decree and Votive Reliefs
26 : 3rd small Room of Votive Reliefs
27 : 4th small Room of Votive Reliefs
28 : Last Grave Monuments of the 4th cent. B.C.
Room of the Youth from Antikythera
29 : Room of « Themis »
30 : 2nd Room of Hellenistic Sculpture
34 : Room of the Altar

CONCORDANCE OF NUMBERS

Inventory number	Page number	Inventory number	Page number	Inventory number	Page number
1	3	39	36	128	67
2	8	40	31	129	68
4	7	41	21	136	101
5	8	42	30	137	101
6	2	43	42	142	102
7	3	44	37	144	103
8	15	45	44	146	102
9	26	46	44	146α	102
10	11	47	64	155	100
11	10	48	13	156	100
12	26	54	41	157	99
12A	26	55	19	158	65
13	19	56	3	159	103
14	11	57	2	160	103
15	8	59	16	161	103
16	26	60	29	162	103
17	27	61	20	163	103
18	27	62	20	173	103
19	26	63	19	174	103
20	27	64	26	175	157
21	9	69	26	176	57
21α	9	71	6	177	67
22	9	72	13	178	163
24	15	73	11	179	163
25	16	76	13	180	163
26	16	81	20	181	168
27	15	83	12	182	165
28	14	84	12	183	160
29	17	85	40	184	160
30	15	86	17	186	165
31	17	87	28	188	119
32	27	88	12	189	158
33	28	89	30	192	162
34	28	93	19	193	122
35	12	96	39	194	159
36	32	115	9	196	172
37	48	126	38	199	53
38	12	127	43	200	67

Inventory number	Page number	Inventory number	Page number	Inventory number	Page number
201	67	248	45	468	53
202	67	251	97	550	162
203	54	252	91	552	188
205	54	253	94	558	61
206	54	254	57	563	192
207	54	255	192	576	124
208	54	257	98	577	124
209	54	258	145	648	43
211	54	259	191	683	93
212	54	260	191	693	134
213	54	262	157	695	134
215	167	265	151	703	138
216	167	274	65	705	66
217	167	275	65	709	129
218	88	299	100	712	46
220	170	303	91	713	47
221	188	313	171	714	51
222	188	317	165	715	50
223	64	318	165	716	47
224	169	322	190	717	83
226	58	323	166	718	84
227	95	324	166	720	89
228	64	327	174	722	113
229	43	332	42	723	82
230	92	351	186	724	84
231	167	354	163	726	81
232	181	362	185	727	73
233	175	363	185	731	108
234	175	364	152	732	71
235	184	366	171	733	34
236	191	379	117	734	35
238	193	380	177	735	35
239	169	381	40	737	119
240	159	383	181	738	125
243	76	429	188	739	36
245	167	438	190	740	35
247	170	457	191	741	35

Inventory number	Page number	Inventory number	Page number	Inventory number	Page number
742	40	829	107	1158	185
743	112	831	80	1184	74
744	113	832	115	1194	183
749	115	833	125	1226	170
751	106	834	117	1239	179
752	83	835	80	1245	75
754	78	869	110	1263	75
763	73	870	109	1283	128
765	78	871	111	1299	128
766	47	873	118	1312	74
770	107	880	47	1313	75
772	108	882	70	1314	75
774	113	884	87	1315	75
775	122	888	116	1317	183
776	2	892	73	1318	182
778	85	896	112	1329	60
779	127	898	112	1332	143
780	190	900	110	1333	141
782	24	901	121	1335	146
793	140	902	79	1338	141
794	89	910	49	1339	142
796	31	922	79	1341	140
803	126	938	117	1343	142
804	126	939	82	1345	146
805	129	941	114	1346	140
806	108	943	129	1351	143
814	111	954	120	1352	143
815	114	966	116	1360	145
817	107	983	74	1367	142
818	107	1005	126	1369	144
819	120	1006	121	1373	142
820	125	1022	110	1377	144
823	116	1028	178	1380	137
824	116	1055	115	1384	149
825	120	1112	56	1385	39
826	111	1154	185	1387	139
828	38	1156	186	1388	142

Inventory number	Page number	Inventory number	Page number	Inventory number	Page number
1389	63	1464	155	1600	96
1390	93	1467	131	1601	96
1391	55	1471	130	1604	96
1392	150	1474	131	1605	23
1394	56	1479	131	1612	64
1395	150	1480	131	1622	66
1397	149	1481	132	1623	158
1402	152	1482	130	1626	98
1403	133	1485	186	1632	187
1404	94	1486	187	1633	68
1408	147	1487	154	1641	72
1419	57	1488	117	1642	72
1420	137	1489	132	1656	162
1421	137	1495	93	1659	181
1422	156	1500	55	1661	182
1424	151	1501	63	1664	43
1425	101	1509	154	1664α	43
1426	151	1519	156	1673	15
1429	148	1558	9	1680	47
1429α	152	1561	59	1688	108
1434	147	1562	59	1731	155
1435	133	1563	59	1732	41
1436	140	1567	59	1733	159
1439	149	1568	59	1734	172
1445	134	1569	59	1735	173
1447	136	1571	58	1736	172
1448	135	1572	59	1737	172
1449	97	1573	59	1738	42
1451	95	1574	59	1751	188
1452	95	1578	58	1752	188
1453	180	1581	59	1753	188
1454	97	1582	59	1754	188
1455	97	1586	9	1755	188
1460	132	1591	96	1762	161
1461	144	1592	96	1763	40
1462	180	1593	96	1772	30
1463	158	1597	97	1776	63

Inventory number	Page number	Inventory number	Page number	Inventory number	Page number
1777	158	1944	23	2546	115
1778	93	1949	39	2557	145
1780	56	1950	134	2565	147
1783	52, 95	1955	81	2569	30
1810	164	1956	81	2574	122
1811	62	1957	128	2578	87
1812	160	1959	22	2582	81
1822	85	1966	92	2583	106
1825	42	1983	128	2584	78
1826	86	1987	74	2585	184
1827	89	1993	84	2588	50
1829	189	2004	84	2589	79
1839	169	2011	135	2592	51
1841	146	2012	135	2594	127
1848	39	2042	84	2611	51
1858	50	2133	162	2650	169
1861	138	2171	173	2651	3
1863	128	2172	173	2667	192
1879	136	2174	173	2668	94
1892	138	2175	173	2670	50
1896	116	2182	66	2687	11
1904	26	2183	66	2702	4
1906	13	2184	67	2720	5
1914	154	2185	67	2723	94
1926	30	2202	157	2728	129
1929	51	2211	140	2743	149
1933	22	2222	171	2744	79
1934	22	2237	181	2756	57
1935	22	2244	124	2772	179
1936	22	2308	89	2779	74
1937	22	2337	39	2811	176
1938	22	2341	27	2814	181
1939	22	2348	54	2823	30
1940	22	2373	147	2824	14
1941	23	2391	179	2825	13
1942	23	2441	147	2826	30
1943	23	2477	141	2869	4

Inventory number	Page number	Inventory number	Page number	Inventory number	Page number
2870	4	3370	23	3602	164
2877	187	3372	5	3605	121
2891	12	3373	177	3614	88
2894	78	3377	190	3617	95
2931	130	3378	113	3619	123
2948	130	3379	50	3622	86
3000	66	3397	99	3624	77
3004	164	3410	55	3645	7
3020	44	3412	163	3645α	6
3043	61	3415	67	3646	56
3044	174	3416	109	3661	72
3045	29	3417	109	3686	16
3069	82	3443	7	3687	24
3071	18	3446	6	3688	183
3072	18	3452	27	3691	121
3073	29	3459	24	3694	124
3074	29	3460	111	3709	51
3076	56	3463	184	3711	24
3131	11	3472	82	3716	118
3153	86	3476	31	3718	65
3156	72	3477	32	3728	15
3205	36	3478	163	3739	66
3245	154	3481	191	3757	23
3246	154	3481α	191	3775	45
3247	154	3485	185	3780	81
3248	183	3486	109	3790	80
3254	49	3488	124	3793	71
3265	62	3500	59	3798	12
3266	176	3526	150	3844	73
3278	52	3534	75	3845	49
3279	63	3552	118	3850	43
3283	87	3556	182	3851	29
3304	148	3569	62	3852	10
3329	147	3572	60	3854	61
3335	189	3574	117	3856	63
3344	34	3579	30	3858	10
3369	149	3586	72	3859	10

Inventory number	Page number	Inventory number	Page number	Inventory number	Page number
3860	11	4465α	92	4519	87
3868	108	4466	92	4526	24
3869	58	4468	29	4527	69
3872	156	4469	12	4531	60
3874	134	4470	49	4537	176
3891	82	4471	4	4539	179
3892	30	4472	20	4545	19
3897	29	4474	13	4546	189
3917	133	4475	35	4547	192
3936	33	4477	26	4553	168
3938	28	4478	36	4642	102
3939	6	4479	36	4762	61
3941	56	4485	48	4763	118
3942	136	4486	64	V. 353	7
3943	98	4487	73	V. 558	18
3947	46	4488	32	V. 804	1
3949	62	4489	8	V. 1955	81
3964	87	4491	69	V. 1956	81
3965	5	4492	101	V. 19567	175
3973	59	4496	124	Br. 6439	177
3989	159	4498	112	Br. 7406	189
3990	34	4502	48	Br. 13396	160
4006	88	4504	18	Br. 13400	178
4008	75	4505	10	Br. 14612	187
4019	162	4506	23	Br. 15161	41
4450	23	4508	176	Br. 15187	161
4464	127	4509	18	Br. 16365	28
4465	91	4516	40	Br. 16513	5

FIRST ROOM OF ARCHAIC SCULPTURE

Instead of the single room which once sheltered all the archaic sculptures (as well as the archaistic !) at the National Museum, in the new post - war arrangement it has seemed necessary to place them in five large and two small rooms. This is not only because new finds have been discovered in the regions of Attica but also because after the storing, pushing and crowding, it has seemed essential that the display of each work should be achieved without damage to its plastic beauty.

A certain number of smaller statues, reliefs and heads have been withdrawn from storage. The picture of archaic art would be less alive if by the side of the major works there were not shown also the secondary rank and the spiritual freshness of the men of that age.

The individuality of the different workshops is principally shown by the Attic Kouroi the majority of which are glowing with a presence full of life ; the island examples have a tender lyric quality, while the Boeotian, though they fall short in quality, beam, the best of them, with an open expression upon the marvels of the world.

Of the Attic grave stelai of the 6th century B.C., some still with vivid colours, the best show a charming carving of the marble. They come to an end about 500 B.C. because of a prohibitive law which checked the progress of the art.

In -the second quarter of the 6th century the cubic character of the statues has passed and they become rich in curves, their outlines more fluid, their faces smiling with a more human expression. In the achievement of this gain, some qualities were lost : the superhuman size, the silent daimonic quality, in several cases the patient care in the carving of the marble, as well as the attention to details combined with the search for grandeur.

V. 804. The large clay amphora from the Dipylon, as one of the earliest purely plastic Hellenic works, has been placed in this room. Its funeral purpose determined the black figures between the handles, the « laying out » of the dead man on the couch, surrounded by mourners. Above him, spread out in creative freedom is the shroud. Behind him in a panel are eight standing mourners.

The varied use of the meander is remarkable. Suitably adapted to the scheme it has different movements, extensions, directions, being a tectonic element. All the decoration, the work of the « painter of the Dipylon », has the precision, and the freedom of the classic geometric style.

It was found in the cemetery of the Kerameikos, outside the Dipylon. The lowest section made up with plaster with the base. Height (total): 1.62 m., height of the neck: 0.50 m.

776. Ivory statuette of a nude goddess with polos on her head. This comes from the same tomb of the Dipylon in which were found the geometric pots and the small ivory figures (in the case against the wall). The smallest of these, a work of « wooden » style, probably by an artist from Syria, served as the model for the fellow artist of Athens who made the goddess no. 776. Fully alive, she has a body with plastic form, vibrating with vitality, and a bright Hellenic eye. About 750 B.C. Height 0.24 m.

6. Statue of a goddess or « heroized » mortal. Seated on a throne she has her hands on her knees. On the front of the base is carved the name Agemo. Cubic form, without curves. It was found « before 1868 » in Arcadia. Marble from Doliana. Work of a local artist. Height 1 m., width in front 0.51 m., on the sides 0.74 m.

57. Statue of a seated goddess or « heroized » mortal. She wears a chiton, and himation, and turns her head, encircled by locks of hair, to the left. Late Daedalic work possibly of a Corinthian or Laconian sculptor, with a suggestion of the turning of the upper body. Of local stone. Found about 1890 at Aghiorgitika, near Tripolis. About 630 B. C. Height of the archaic part 0.89 m., maximum width 0.52 m. (P l. 1).

7. A woman seated on a stool — two parts of the lower body. She wears a peplos or chiton and short himation, it covers her arms which are joined to her body. There is a delicate indication of the folds. Very early, of cubic form, the work of an island sculptor. Made up with plaster. Found near the Dipylon (1870), it would have been a sepulchral statue for a tomb of the Kerameikos. End of the 7th century B. C. Height 0.76 m., length 0.63 m., width below in front 0.41 m.

1. Statue of Artemis from Delos (1878). It is of the « xoanon » type with pendent arms and feet together. She wears a long, closely girded chiton. The locks of her hair frame her face and her long neck.

According to the inscription engraved below on the narrow left side, the statue was consecrated to the goddess by « Nikandra of Naxos, the most important among all women, the daughter of Deinodokos, the sister of Deinomenes the wife of Phraxos ». Work of a Naxian sculptor representing the Daedalic style in its island expression. One of the older marble statues. About 650 B. C. Height 1.90 m.

56. Sepulchral monument of poros. The two deceased young men are represented in high relief,in the type of Kouroi in an embrace. According to the inscription carved on the base Amphalkes (the father?) erected it on the tomb of Dermys and Kitylos. Above there would have been the statue of a Sphinx. A simple but warmly expressive work of a Boeotian sculptor. About the middle of the 6th century B.C. Brought from Tanagra in 1887. Height (total) 2 m., height of figures 1.47 m. (Pl. 2 a).

2651. Head of a Kouros of local stone. A narrow band around the hair. The tresses of the hair cut to fall as far as the neck. The forehead is narrow. It was found in 1905 in the village of Lepreon in Arcadia. The work of a local stone cutter. Toward the end of the 7th century B. C. Height 0.18 m.

METOPES FROM THE ARCHAIC TEMPLE OF ATHENA AT MYCENAE

2869. Fragment of a metope of poros. The upper body of a goddess, toward the right, the head facing forward. She wears a girded peplos. With her left hand she held the edge of a cloak which covered her head as well. Above her low forehead a double row of curved locks. The face, slightly turned to the right, is surrounded by thick tresses, the arrangement in horizontal sections (P l. 2 b).

The vibrant characteristics of the face underlined by a square chin with strong projection. A radiant work, probably of a Corinthian sculptor of the late Daedalic style. About 630 B.C. Height 0.39 m., width 0.29 m.

2870. This is the best preserved of the other metopes. The lower bare body of a nude youth and one foot of an animal which lifts the body with a clawed hoof. On the left, above the body, the foot of another animal (Genii of death?). The metopes were found in 1886.

4471. This fragment was found much later than the others (1955). There is preserved the crest of a helmet and the hand of a warrior under the flat epistyle. Height 0.28 m., width 0.46 m.

2702. The lower part of an octagonal column of poros. It is joined with the unevenly squared base (only on the sides are the four edges prominent). In front and behind is the broader plane surface of the column. The upper section is sawn obliquely. Found at the Argive Heraion and was formerly thought to be an aniconic cult statue. Height 0.91 m.

SECOND ROOM OF ARCHAIC SCULPTURE

Br. 16513. Bronze statuette of a flute player (probably a mellephebe, a very young man) with its square plinth. Dressed in a long chiton he puts forward his left leg and raises his head, extending forward his two arms which hold a double flute. The face is surrounded by the straps of the flute (the halter), the hair falls low on his back. The outlines flow rhythmically at the back and also on the lower body in the two side views. It was dedicated at the Heraion of Samos where it was found in 1925 with a serious decay on its surface. It has been conserved by electrolysis.

This bronze statue, cast solid, probably suggests the hypothesis that bronze casting, « à cire perdue », the important discovery of Theodoros of Samos, did not yet exist then, at a date of about 540 B.C., or was not generally known. Height 0.42 m.

3372. The « Dipylon Head ». It belonged to a statue of a sepulchral Kouros of over life size placed above a tomb of the Kerameikos. Traces of red colour in the bands which gird the hair. The locks fall low at the back. All the planes are broad, cubic, impressive. Found in 1916. A great work of about 610 B.C. The Kouros was one of the oldest Attic examples. To the statue belongs also the arm no. **3965** (in the wall case, worthy of the head in its charming carving). Height of the head 0.42 m. (Pl. 3).

2720. Statue of a Kouros of over life size with its plinth and base. It is of the customary type, with left leg advanced, pendent arms. The face is geometrically constructed with broad flat planes at the sides, a powerful chin. The hair falls at the back bound by a band which becomes twofold about the curled locks on the forehead and is fastened

3

at the back in a « Heraklean » knot. The excessively large
linear ears give a grandeur to the face. The muscular modelling is remarkable, the linear indications of anatomical
details have an expressive breadth. Noteworthy is the
oblique position of the Kouros on its base (harmonizing with
another corresponding Kouros). Found at Sounion in 1906.
It stood in front of the temple of Poseidon together with
other similar ones (see no. **3645** and the neighbouring bases nos **3939** and **3645α**). A little later than the Dipylon
Head. About 600 B.C. (Pl. 4).

3645a, 3939. Two bases for Kouroi, square. Fastened
above them with lead is the plinth with the two feet (on
the larger and better preserved, no. 3645a). On no. 3939
is preserved the right foot and traces of the other. The
base is damaged as well as the back of the plinth. The feet
of no. 3645a have an obvious slant to the left. About
600 B.C.

3645a: Height of the base 0.22 m., breadth in front 0.84
m., at the sides 0.90 m. Length of the plinth from the
sides· 0.85 m.

3939. Breadth of the base 0.73 m., length 0.87 m., height
0.21 m. Found at Sounion in 1906 together with the large
Kouroi in the same room.

3446. Small head of an archaic Kore with a narrow encircling band. All the back view smooth. Lively Attic work
of the beginning of the 6th century B.C. Found at Sounion,
in the Temple of Athena in 1916. Height 0.115 m.

71. Torso of a funerary Kouros. Found in the cemetery
of the Kerameikos in 1887. From the head there is extant
only the rear part with the locks of hair which fall on the
back. The formation still cubic. The anatomy of the abdomen without plastic rendering has a primitive grace. Attic,
about 580 B.C. Height 0.77 m.

V. 353. « Piraeus Amphora ». Large black - figured funerary amphora. On its thick neck a cock. On the body two chariots facing right, one in front of the other, with two horses each. In the chariot the charioteer holds the reins. The large bodies of the horses and their inflexible « wooden » feet, as well as the scheme of the amphora have the simple grandeur of the works of the proto-Attic style about 630 B.C., with the influence of the proto-Corinthian models in the predominance of the silhouette over the outline. Conical foot. The site where it was found (according to the inventory of the Museum): Athens or Piraeus. Height 1.08 m.

3645. Torso of a statue of a Kouros of over life size. Vigorous plastic modelling of the shoulders, the chest, and of the pelvis, the fascinating linear portrayal of the anatomy of the 'abdomen, and of the back. Slender waist. Extant is the part of the hair which falls at the back, the locks of which, separated perpendicularly, end in spirals.

Found at Sounion in 1906 with the Kouros no. 2720 and the adjacent bases. Upper parts of the arms were attached in 1958. Work of the same artist who created the Kouros no. 2720, a little smaller but with more plastic grandeur in the body, it was placed in the same place as the other. About 600 B.C. Height 1.65 m.

4. Statuette of a woman. She wears a girded peplos, the breasts visible («deep-girded»). The hands fall at the sides with open palms. Two simple strands of hair on each side of the neck. It belongs together with two similar statuettes (one on the same wall no. **3443**) to the support of a « periranterion ». A head in the Thebes Museum belongs to this statuette. Found in 1886 at the sanctuary of Ptoan Apollo. The archaic cubic construction and the religious connection have an agreeable sympathy with the plastic conception. End of the 7th century B.C. Height 0.42 m.

2. Torso of a statue (of Apollo Kitharodos ?, with the kithara) of a rectangular archaic type. He wears a long (foot-length) chiton girded high at the waist and a himation. A large part of the lower body restored. Remains of the dedicatory inscription (boustrophedon), with the end of the name of the stone cutter «...τος ἐποίεσεν». Of local poros. Found in 1885 in the sanctuary of Ptoan Apollo (Boeotia). End of the 7th century B.C. Total height including the plinth 1.52 m.

15. Head of a Kouros, of poros. The forehead high, the hair poorly carved falls at the back. A Boeotian work, somewhat careless, but very expressive, dependent on an Attic model. Found in 1885 in the sanctuary of Ptoan Apollo. About 580 B.C. Height 0.30 m.

5. Statuette of a Kore, headless. She wears a peplos, girded, with short overlap. Two bands from the belt fall down on the abdomen. Three simple locks of hair on each shoulder, the hair high on the back. A provincial work, typical of the beginning of the 6th century B.C. Found at Eleusis in 1882. Height 0.36 m.

4489. Head of a Kouros statue. All of the surface of the face is battered. Preserved in better condition are the locks of hair on the neck with very light identations, and above the temples are other tresses, spirals. Fine Cycladic art about 540 B.C. Unknown provenance. Height 0.29 m.

1558. Statue of a sepulchral Kouros with its plinth. Found on Melos in 1891. A tender work of an island sculptor, one of the most attractive of its period. The arms without energy, lifeless. About 550 B.C. The surface corroded with salt. Height 2.14 m. (Pl. 5).

115. Head of a small Kouros (?). The face flat at the sides. Poor state of preservation. Delicate Cycladic work of about 550 B.C. Found on Melos in 1865. Height 0.21 m.

1586. Head of a Kouros of over life size, with long hair. Found on Melos. Excellent, expressive work of an island sculptor of about 550 B.C. The surface much corroded. Height 0.32 m.

21. Statue of a winged Victory, who runs toward the left in the archaic manner. She wears a girded chiton. By the baring of the right leg the folds are gathered together between her legs. On her head a rich crown in the holes of which were fastened bronze ornaments, likewise earrings in holes. One wing, in the back view, rests on the right ankle. Found on Delos (1877), and it was an offering to the precinct of Apollo. Cheerful, important work of an islander, probably of a Parian sculptor, with beautiful carving. About 550 B.C. Height 0.90 m. (Pl. 6). See the adjacent inscribed plaque no. 21a.

21a. Inscribed base of a statue, with a hollow for the insertion of the plinth. The rest of the inscription mentions the Chian sculptor Archermos, possibly also Mikkiades. It is not certain whether the adjacent Victory, no. 21, was placed on this base. Found on Delos. Height 0.14 m., width 0.53 m.

22. Statue of a Kore of the Acropolis type. By the side of her left leg which appears there is a perpendicular cluster of folds of her diaphanous chiton. The fully pleated himation, spread out, covers all her body. Many holes on the chest for the fastening of the ends of her locks of hair. A necklace. It is developed only from the front view, the back plane not worked. The right arm from another piece of marble is added. A rich work with excellent carving from the hand of a Cycladic sculptor, probably Parian. End of the 6th century B.C. Found on Delos, about 1879. Height 1.34 m.

4505. Statue of a Kouros of alabaster. Found in Cyprus. Contrary to the Greek manner of the nude Kouroi, he wears an Ionian chiton, diaphanous, which extends to the ankles. Surface worn. Work of a local sculptor with Ionian influence. About 530 B.C. Height 0.47 m.

11. Torso of a votive Kouros. The arms were fastened above close to the body. Distinctive rendering of the anatomic formation. Delicate work of a Cycladic (probably Naxiote) sculptor, about 560 B. C. Found in the sanctuary of Ptoan Apollo in Boeotia (1885). Height 0.82 m.

3858. Torso of a Kouros with long narrow neck, and with its head. The hair bound with a band falls at the back. Work probably of an island sculptor (probably Naxiote (?)). About 580 B.C. Found in Athens, Moschato (1938). Height 0.67 m.

3859. Upper body of a statue of a Kore with chiton. The arm horizontal in front of the chest. The border of the chiton is carved perpendicularly from the throat. Work of an island sculptor about 580 B.C. with reminiscence of cubic formation at the sides. Probably from Athens. Height 0.40 m.

3852. Torso of a small Kouros. A band carved round the throat. The hair dressed behind with schematic, diagonally balanced locks. Traces of the old cubic formation. The plain chest, has a plastic vitality. About 570 B. C. Found at Markopoulo in Attica. Height 0.305 m.

10. Statue of a votive Kouros, from the sanctuary of Ptoan Apollo (Boeotia). Work of a Cycladic (Naxiote?) sculptor, with eastern influence. About 560 B.C. Height 1.30 m.

3860. Torso of a Kouros. There is only a little preserved from the locks of hair at the back. The surface battered. About 550 B. C. Found in Athens (1938). Height 0.75 m.

14. Unfinished statue of a Kouros. Found on Naxos in 1835. It is noteworthy that the sculptor of the archaic period worked in the round at each stage of the carving with a plastic sense. The legs are missing. About 540 B.C. Height 1.02 m.

3131. Part of a small but heavy pediment of poros. On the crumbling surface are preserved three figures: in the centre a dancing Maenad, on the left a Satyr flute player, on the right another. About the middle of the 6th century B.C. Found in the theatre of Dionysos. It would have belonged probably to the older temple of the god. Height 0.54 m., length 0.90 m.

73. The upper torso of a statue of a goddess or Kore of over-life size. The head is missing. She wears a sleeved chiton with engraved borders. Four strands of hair on the shoulders, others behind. It is one of the earliest statues of the type with remnants of robust archaic cubic construction. About 570 B.C. Found on Aegina. Height 0.42 m.

2687. Large grave stele, rectangular. Broken off in ancient times for building into the Themistoclean wall of the Kerameikos. Nude youth with a spear, facing right. Below, separated into a zone, a running Gorgon (the border ornament of the chiton is preserved). Above there would have been a surmounting Sphinx. Important Attic work about 560 B.C. Found in the Kerameikos in 1905. Height 2.395 m.

2891. Statue of a Sphinx, with a large wing, once coloured (the colours preserved at the back). A band around the hair (traces of colour). The locks of hair fall at the back. It was above the upper part of an archaic stele (adjacent pla ster cast). Found in 1906 in the Kerameikos, built into the Themistoclean wall of the city. The edges of the wing were found in the excavations of recent years. An Attic work, full of life by one of the foremost sculptors around 550 B.C. Height 0.485 m., length 0.535 m.

35. The middle part of an archaic grave stele in relief. The body is preserved with the hanging arm fastened to the thigh, with the fingers extended toward the back. 560-550 B.C. Found in Athens, in 1872. Height 0.47 m.

84. The upper part of a grave stele, restored. Two large carved spirals, antithetic, with the outer outline in a curve. At their centre a petal from a palmette hangs downward. Above the abacus a Sphinx would have stood. About 550 B.C. Found built into the wall of the Dipylon. Height 0.50 m.

3798. Face of an archaic Kouros or Sphinx with corroded surface. Found in 1937 in Athens, near the Kerameikos. 550-540 B.C. Height 0.20 m.

38. Part of a grave stele. The deceased is represented as an athlete who holds the diskos above his head. The hair behind is in an attractive hair-net. An important, radiant work of about 560 B.C. of the « Rampin sculptor » with wonderful marble carving. Found in the Dipylon in 1873. Height 0.34 m. From the same stele probably comes the part of a leg, no. **83** adjacent (Pl. 7).

88 and **4469**. Fragments of a large relief, probably sepulchral. Composed from an old acquisition and from a much later addition. It is difficult to interpret the unusual theme. The left figure seems to be seated, the other behind standing. In some places the folds are rendered in incisions, in others freely carved in relief. End of the 6th century B.C. From Attica. No. 88 was found in 1840, the other in 1957. The re-uniting is due to the sculptor St. Triantis. Height 0.47 m., width 0.53 m.

4474. Part of a grave stele of an athlete carved in relief. The subject is a replica of the adjacent stele of the Diskophoros from the Dipylon, no. 38. Standing, facing right, he holds in his left hand the diskos behind his head. The surface is damaged by the rounding off of the relief for its second use. Found on the site of Phoenikia in the plain of Attica, given in 1958 by the owner El. Melissourgos. About 530 B.C. Height 1.101 m., width above 0.43 m., below 0.45 m.

72. Statue of a small sepulchral Kouros, headless. About 540 B.C. Found probably in the Kerameikos. Height 0.44 m.

1906. Statue of a sepulchral Kouros. Above the forehead flamelike locks toward the top, the hair bound at the back with a band between the ears, falls high on the back which is plastically divided into two sections. Attic work of unusually noble delicacy and charm. About 550 B.C. Found at Volomandra (Kalyvia Kouvara) in Attica (1903). Height 1.78 m.

BALANCE WRONG

48. Face of a statue of a Kouros. Above the forehead flamelike locks of hair. About 550 B.C. Probably from Aegina. Height 0.32 m.

2825. Upper part of a rectangular grave stele. Of the relief there is preserved only the top of the head of a man. Higher up his spear can be distinguished carved obliquely. About 550 B.C. Found in 1907, built into the Themistoclean Wall of the Kerameikos. Height 0.56 m.

76. Statue of a Sphinx, the top of a grave stele. Round

the hair a band with carved (formerly also coloured) meander. About 540 B.C. Found in Piraeus in 1880. Height 0.79 m·

28. Statue of an archaic Sphinx, facing right, with polos on the head, and with a necklace. It was placed as a roof above a grave stele. Found in the village of Spata in Attica and is of local origin, a somewhat rough, provincial work. About 570 B.C. Height 0.66 m., length 0.54 m.

2824. The back left leg of a wild animal resting on the plinth. The formation of the sides in planes. Found in 1906 built into the Themistoclean Wall of the Kerameikos (compare in the same room nos. 2687, 2891). Height 0.27 m., width 0.31 m.

4889   Kore from Meranda in left hand.

4890   Kouros from Meranda

8. Statue of a funerary Kouros. The legs from the knees are missing. The arms awkwardly joined to the body. The hair falls high at the back. Broad band around the head. Crude carving. Found on Thera on 1836. Height 1.24 m.

3728. Small square Hermaic stele, ithyphallic, and with the head of a bearded Hermes. Excellent island work about 520 B.C. From Siphnos. Height 0.66 m.

24. Statue of a Kore of Acropolis type. Crown around the head. Spiral curls above her forehead, her hair falls low on her back (its red colour preserved). Provincial work around 490 B.C. Found at Eleusis, the torso in 1883, the head in 1888. Height 0.69 m. (Pl. 9 a).

1673. Half section of a group. A lion tears the hind part of a bull. Made up with plaster. The other half (the second lion and the head of the victim) is in the Metropolitan Museum. The part in the National Museum was found in 1862 in Athens near the Olympeion. The whole would probably have been the pediment of the archaic temple within the precinct of the Pythian Apollo. Attic, of the late archaic period about 500 B. C. The mane has successive rows of flame pattern. Length of the marble 0.73 m., total with the plaster reconstruction 1.40 m., height 0.60 m. (P l. 11 b).

27. Head of an archaic Kore. Above the high forehead and in front of the ears are locks of red hair, others fall to the shoulders. Round earrings (on one green ornaments). The skin is delicately worked. End of the 6th century B.C. Found at Eleusis in 1882. Height 0.21 m.

30. Grave stele formerly coloured, with the broad base. It lacks the upper end. According to the inscription carved on the base it was placed on the tomb of Lyseas by his father Semon. Lyseas holds the sacred vase of Dionysos, the kantharos. ·Below a small predella with a galloping horseman, this likewise coloured. Found in 1839 at Velanideza in Attica. About 500 B.C. Height of the stele 1.96 m., width below 0.48 m., height of the base 0.28 m., width 0.72 m.

26. Statue of a Kore, headless. Above the chiton with its fluttering folds she wears a himation of which the edges are brought together in front with doubly arranged pleats. In her lowered left hand she holds the edge of the chiton, in the other which is missing she would have held a flower or a bird. The left leg advances slightly. Her hair (with traces of red) falls down her back, three locks on each shoulder. Good careful carving, the fanciful archaic dress rather simplified. Beginning of the 5th century B. C. Found at Eleusis in 1882. Height 0.56 m. (P l. 9 b).

59. Small head of a statuette of a Kore. A double row of curled locks on the forehead, others waved, fall down on each side of her neck. Found at Eleusis in 1887. Height 0.12 m.

3686. Statue of a sepulchral Kouros. The legs heavy, separated the one from the other. The anatomical formation developed, the chest showing strong plastic prominence. Band around the head, the locks of hair centred at the back, others spiral, large, above the high forehead. Brave work of an island ·sculptor (Parian?). About 530 B.C. Found on Keos (Tzia) in 1930. The arms and parts of the lower body restored. Height of the ancient part 1.73. m. (P l. 10).

25. Statuette of a headless Kore, of archaic type. The hair falls low at the back, the locks on the chest. The left arm from another piece of marble. Found at Eleusis in 1882. Height 0.44 m.

86. Grave stele of Antiphanes. Slight, joined with lead to the square base. It ends above with spirals and a blossom with leaves turned back. The painting is now effaced. A cock to the right. Below is carved the name of the deceased in the genitive : 'Ἀντιφάνους. About 520 B.C. Found in Athens (Aeolus Street). Total height 1.56 m., without the base 1.37 m.

31. Large grave stele — the lower part. Preserved, amid the red colouring of the ground, a white horseman facing right. Above, the remains of the relief, feet of the deceased towards the right. Black around the periphery. About 500 B.C. Found in Athens (Aeolu Street). Height 0.45 m., depth 0.15 m.

29. Grave stele of Aristion. Tall and narrow, with a light frame. Joined with lead to its quadrangular base. The deceased is represented as a hoplite, bearded, facing right, with a light chiton, thorax, helmet, and greaves. In his left hand he grasps a spear, the other hand hangs down. With bare feet he stands to the edge towards the side, where the name of the sculptor was carved: "Ἔργον 'Ἀριστοκλέους. High on the base the name of the deceased in the genitive : 'Ἀριστίωνος (red colour on the letters). The upper crown of the stele is missing, with the top of the helmet. One of the principal works of the late archaic period probably about 500 B.C. (therefore not a Marathon warrior). The rendering of the anatomy of the body and of the pleats is excellent. Spiral curls on the forehead and the neck. The hairs of his beard are portrayed with fascinating accuracy. On his face terracotta colour. Traces of red at the bottom of the slab. Traces of coloured decoration on the thorax. Found in 1839 at Velanideza in Attica, not far from the stele of Lyseas, no. 30. Height of the stele 2.02 m., width 0.14 m. Height of the base 0.24 m., width 0.72 m., depth 0.43 m. (Pl. 8).

3072. Mask of Dionysos. He is bearded with drooping moustache. Spiral tresses with a strong plastic elevation above a low forehead. It lacks the central part of the face and part of the beard. The carving of the rest bears witness that this brave work is from the hand of one of the best sculptors of archaic Athens. About 520 B.C. It was found at Dionysos (Ikaria) in Attica in 1888. It provided the face of « Dionysos of the tree ». It was hung on the trunk of a tree while the rest of the body was indicated by a long chiton and a himation which covered the trunk. Height 0.41 m., width 0.35 m. (Pl. 11a).

4504. The lower part of a mask, of a « Dionysos of the tree ». The beard, curved below, has strands lightly worked. Attic work, about 480 B.C. Provenance unknown. See no. 3072. Height 0.067 m., length 0.095 m.

3071. Grave stele of a hoplite, tall and narrow, rectangular, with a light frame. It lacks the upper part with his head. He was represented in the style of the Aristion, no. 29, facing right, grasping a spear in his left hand. Traces of a painted meander on the chiton. About 520 B.C. It was found at Stamata in Attica in 1888. Height 1.71 m., width 0.48 m.

V. 558. Funerary amphora, black figured. In the panel zone a black Corinthian helmet with high crest. A wreath of myrtle incised around the helmet panel. All the rest of the body of the pot is covered with a gleaming black glaze. It was used as a container for the half burned bones of the deceased. About 550 B.C. Provenance unknown. Height 0.61 m.

4509. Head of a statue of a Kouros. Very high forehead. The construction of the face has cubic traces, the lips are long and smiling. The representation of the hair at the back is irregular. The work, carved probably by a Parian

sculptor, has an island tenderness. Middle of the 6th century B.C. Found at Megara. The marble is battered at various points. Height 0.32 m.

55. Fragment of a heavy plaque with a funeral feast (νε-
κρόδειπνον) in deep relief. On the left a goddess, seated on a
throne, with her left hand lifts her himation in front of her
face. In her other hand she holds a flower. In the centre a standing nude youth facing right holds a wreath. Further to the
right is the leg of a bed upon which is visible the foot of
a man laying extended. Below is the edge of a table. Probably Laconian work of about 560 B.C. It was found, built
into a wall in 1878 in a house in the vicinity of Tegea.
Height 0.40 m.; width 0.38 m., depth 0.18 m.

13. Torso of a Kouros of over life size. The arms would
have been separated from the body at the waist. The anatomy of the abdomen is both plastic and developed. An
advanced radiant Kouros of about 540 B. C. Found at
Megara in 1860. Height 2 m.

4545. The left calf of the Kouros of Megara. It has a
strong plastic form, while the outer details of the anatomy are shown by deeply carved grooves. Brought from
the Megara Museum in 1965. Height 0.55 m.

63. Head of a Kouros with a high round skull. A band
between the ears holds his hair. A powerful expressive
work of a Peloponnesian sculptor. About 540 B.C. Found
at Palaia Epidauros. Height 0.34 m.

93. Small marble disk. According to the inscription carved around it, it was consecrated to the memory of the « wise
and excellent doctor Aeneas» who was one of the ancestors
of Hippocrates. Only traces are preserved of the painting
of Aeneas, represented seated on a chair, facing right. A-
bout 500 B.C. Found in Piraeus in 1889. Unknown provenance. Diam. 0.27 m.

4472. Fragment of a funeral stele. The front part of the face of a female (?) figure is preserved. With her long left hand, from behind, she holds the head of a child who looks toward her. In front of his face is the painted border of the himation of the first figure. Plentiful traces of red colour on the surface. The theme is unique on archaic stelai. An exceptional Attic monument about 530 B.C. It was found in 1958 at Anavyssos in Attica. Height 0.385 m., length 0.44 m.

81. Base of a funerary monument. It consists of three graduated steps of poros, with considerable depth in the lowest. On the front of the fourth, the highest (this one is of marble), the « epigram » is carved in large beautiful letters ; it says that the monument was set up by the father above the grave of his daugther Phile and was made by the sculptor Phaidimos. Of the statue there is extant a part of the plinth, with the edges of the feet — the toes delicate — with high sandals. About 550 B.C. Found in the village Vourva in Attica, it would have been one of the finest monuments of the Mesogeia in Attica. Height of the low base 0.27 m., width 1.22 m., height of the remaining steps together 0.93 m., height of the plinth with the feet 0.15 m.

62. Head of a statue of a Kore, with band around the hair. Three holes for the attachment of a metal band on the forehead. A somewhat provincial sculpture, with retarded cubic formation. About 540 B.C. Found at Eleusis (1884). Height 0.16 m.

61. Head probably from a statue of a horseman. It has a marked turning and tension of the neck toward the right. Band around the head. Somewhat hard but of good technique, with accurate working of the locks of hair. A pleasant, smiling Attic work of about 560 B.C., with remains of cubic modelling. Found at Eleusis in 1887. Height 0.18 m.

41. « Cavetto » capital of a grave stele in relief (above it would have been placed a Sphinx). Engraved and relief decoration on the abacus and lower, above and around the representation in relief of a horseman facing right (the deceased), with two horses. On the narrow side are visible two mourning singers and the father. Colours effaced. About 550 B.C. It has the charm of the earlier sculptures of the 6th century B. C. Found in the village of Lambrika (ancient Lamptrai) in Attica. Height 0.74 m.

1933 - 38. Heads of warriors, from the Temple of Aphaia on Aegina (excavations of 1901). They belonged to the archaic eastern pediment and were buried under the temple when, a little later, for some unknown reason all the figures of this pediment were replaced by later ones (which are now in the Glyptothek in Munich). The warriors wear the Corinthian helmet, raised. Radiant works of the Aeginetan school with something of the brilliance of the island's famous bronze technique. About 500 B.C. In no. 1933, the holes in the forehead and beside the ear served to hold in position the beard which was of another piece of marble, as also the locks of hair. Height 0.28 m. In no. 1938, the latest of all, the strands of the beard were rendered with colour. Height 0.23 m. (Pl. 13 a - b).

1939. Head of a Kouros, or smiling Sphinx, with the neck framed by locks of hair. From the side a simple plane. Ionian work of about 550 B.C. Found on Aegina in 1901. Height 0.22 m.

1940. Small head of a statue of a goddess (?). The hair bound together at the back in a snood. Good Aeginetan work of the severe style, about 480 B.C. Found in the temple of Aphaia on Aegina. Height 0.14 m.

1959. Relief of a running hoplite. He is represented nude with Attic helmet in the archaic manner of a runner, the legs side view to the right, the chest frontal, the head facing left. Carved with marvellous plastic feeling and with care the development of the figure on the surface is very clear. Found in Athens, in 1902 (?) near the Theseion. Uncertain whether it would have been part of a funeral monument or an independent grave stele. According to a recent opinion a Pyrrhic dancer is represented. An Attic relief about 500 B.C., one of the best of the period. Height 1 m., width below 0.75 m. above 0.73 m. (as far as the edges of the spirals) (Pl. 12).

In the case. **1941 - 44.** Arms and hands from statues of warriors from the pediments of the Temple of Aphaia on Aegina. Found in 1901. Length 0.15 m. and 0.13 m.

4450. The right hand of a statue of a warrior from the pediments, holding a spear. The articulation of the fingers is charming. Found in 1951 on Aegina, below the west pediment of the temple of Aphaia. Height 0.65 m., length 0.15 m.

4506. The right arm of a large statue of Athena, probably a cult statue. The clasped fingers held a spear. Above are holes, probably for the fixing of the aegis. Provenance unknown. It is probable that it belongs to the Aeginetan sculptures, not however to the pediments. Width 0.35 - 0.36 m.

3370. Torso of a statue of a Kouros. The anatomy of the sides has a plastic accentuation, the marked elevation of the back shows progress, but the formation of the area of the abdomen is undeveloped. Strong, soundly constructed Attic work of the end of the 6th century B.C. Found in 1914 at Aghios Kosmas on the coast of Attica. Height 0.67 m.

1605. The « Daphni Torso ». Torso of a nude warrior (more probable than of an athlete). He falls toward the back and right, with a marked reverse turning of the left shoulder. Skilled rendering of the anatomy. An excellent Attic work, round 490 B.C., it probably comes from some pediment. Found near Daphni. Height 0.73 m.

3757. Torso of a Kouros. Delicate formation of the abdomen, chest, and pelvis, with slight projection. The hair behind flat. About 530 B.C. Unknown provenance. Height 0.75 m.

3711. Statue of a god seated on a stool (of « camp stool » type). On the sides of the figure dark colour is preserved, by which the skin of a panther is indicated (red background, the same red also on the high footstool). The god wears a himation, closely wrapped around his body. The left hand would have held a vase. Splendid formation of the toes and the calves of the legs, as well as of the whole work. Flat planes on the sides and from the back view. There is doubt whether Dionysos or Zeus is represented. Work of a leading sculptor of Athens about 500 B.C. Found in 1931 in Athens (Piraeus Street). Total height 1.07 m., height of the base above the sides 0.13 m. Maximum depth of the statue 0.61 m.

782. Finial of a grave stele, late archaic. Above the spirals a palmette with nine carved petals. On the left the petals are of a pale red a ternating with a dark colour. On the right the pale colour alternates with white. Formerly traces of blue were preserved. Found in the Kerameikos. A delicate work with Ionian influence. End of the 6th century B.C. Height 0.43 m.

4526. The lower part of a grave stele. The carved outlines of the feet of a youth facing right are preserved, the toes well articulated. Black colour accents the carving, the background of the plaque is red. About 550 B. C. Unknown provenance. Height 0.26 m., thickness 0.085 m.

3687. The « Kouros of the Ilissos ». Torso of a male statue (Hermes?). He wears a short chlamys which leaves bare the front part of the body and falls in schematic folds. Charming Attic work with Ionian influence. Beginning of the 5th century B.C. Found in the bed of the Ilissos in 1930· Maximum height 0.65 m. (P l. 14).

3459. Head of a conquered warrior. The tongue protrudes slightly, between the pressed lips. The square head has an unusual depth. Work of an Argive artist, about 470 B.C. Found in 1920 on Aegina, near the Temple of Aphrodite. Probably from a pediment. Height 0.17 m., length 0.17 m.

4477. Palmette from an archaic grave stele with surrounding petals. Fine Attic art of about 510 B.C. It was built into the wall of the chapel of the Saints Theodoroi, Koukouvaounes, in Attica. Height 0.63 m.

64. Head of a votive Kouros from Delphi. Crude but not unexpressive, of native stone, with Peloponnesian influence. About 530 B.C. Height 0.23 m.

1904. Statue of a sepulchral Kouros, unfinished. It was found at Keratea in Attica. Crude work of a local marble worker about 550 B.C. Height 1.43 m.

12. Statue of a Kouros, offering to the sanctuary of Ptoan Apollo in Boeotia. The arms slightly bent. A cheerful late archaic work of a Boeotian sculptor of the end of the 6th century B.C. Possibly the feet on the plinth nearby (no. **12 A**) belong to this statue. Height 1.60 m.

69. Small torso of a Kouros from chest to knees. The right arm is also missing. Found in 1885 in the sanctuary of Ptoan Apollo in Boeotia. Simple, local art. Height 0.51 m.

16. Head of a statue of a votive Kouros. The outer surface smooth. Found in 1885 in the sanctuary of Ptoan Apollo (Boeotia). By the hand of a native sculptor carved with Ionic sense. Height 0.186 m.

19. Head of a Kouros (all the back is missing), surrounded by a light band in a groove. Found in the sanctuary of Ptoan Apollo in Boeotia in 1886. Expressive work of a Boeotian sculptor. About 550 B.C. Height 0.20 m.

9. Statue of a Kouros of Boeotian marble. A fillet around the head, the face without expression. Provincial, by a Boeo-

tian marbleworker. Known since 1860, when it was kept
in a monastery at Orchomenos. Height 1.27 m.

18. Head of a Kouros, of poros. The hair falls low at the
back, below the neck. The face is long with battered surface. A crude work, of a local marbleworker, about 540
B.C. Found in the sanctuary of Ptoan Apollo (Boeotia)
in 1886. Height 0.27 m.

32. Part of a grave stele of two men. According to the inscription engraved below the relief it was placed above the
grave of Agathon and Aristokrates. In front the lower nude
body of one and the left hand which holds an apple or a
rose. Behind is sketched the body of the other youth, clothed
in a himation as far as the ankles. Found at Thespiae in
1865. Good work of a Boeotian sculptor, about 500 B.C.
Height 1.04 m., width 0.44 m.

3452. Small head of a Kouros with remains of cubic construction. Crude but not lifeless, around 550 B.C. The upper
part of the face battered. Found in the sanctuary of Ptoan
Apollo in Boeotia. Height 0.20 m.

20. Statue of a votive Kouros. The lower part is lacking.
Found in the sanctuary of Ptoan Apollo in Boeotia (1885).
According to the inscriptions engraved on the thighs it was
dedicated to the « god of the silver bow » by Pytheas and
Aiskhrion. Expressive work of a Boeotian sculptor with Io-
nian influence. About 500 B.C. Height 1.03 m.

2341. The lower part of the head of a Kouros, of po-
ros. End of the 6th century B.C. Found in the sanctuary of
Ptoan Apollo. From the hand of a local marble - worker.
Height 0.12 m.

17. Head of a Kore with high crown, with round ear -
rings. Locks of hair encircle her face, lacking colours.
Boeotian work, crude but not without life, influenced by Attic Korai. End of the 6th century. Height 0.23 m.

33. Part of an archaic stele. The upper body of a hoplite facing right. The surface badly preserved. Known since 1858, when it was built into the wall of a small Attic church. A rough work of about 510 B.C. Height 0.79 m., width 0.47 m.

34. The lower part of an Attic grave stele. The legs of a hoplite toward the right, with greaves. On the bare plane, below, a figure was painted. About 520 B.C. Found in Athens (Aeolos Street) in 1871. (It is not from the adjacent stele no. 33). Height 0.95 m., thickness 1.17 m.

87. Part of an Attic grave stele. Of the beautiful relief there is preserved part of the right arm and a little of the body of a young man facing right. Red colour on the polished surface. About 520 B.C. Found in the Dipylon in 1889. Height 0.33 m.

3938. Sepulchral Kouros with the plinth and the square base. The name, in the genitive, is engraved on the base without the patronymic : ’Αριστοδίκο. A nude man of the advancing type of Kouros, the arms bent. The short hair at the back ends high on the neck. Faint traces of red colour on the crown of the head. Around the plinth remains of the lead which strengthened the base. Parian marble, the base Pentelic. It was found in the Mesogeia of Attica and brought to the Museum in 1944. A radiant Attic creation, full of life, well constructed. It is one of the last archaic Kouroi, about 500 B.C. Height 1.98 m., of the base 0.29 m. Length of the base 0.72 m., width 0.53 m. (Pl. 15).

Br. 16365. Small bronze statue with its square base. Apollo is represented as Epiphenomenos (Appearing), nude with the left leg forward. It was found in the village of Kosmas near Sparta. An attractive product of a Laconian workshop. End of the 6th century B.C. Height 0.18 m.

60. Head of a statue of a Kore (running?). A wide band, once coloured, around the head. Five sets of curled locks with rich clusters around the temples. End of the archaic period, about 490 B. C. Found at Eleusis in 1887. Height 0.16 m.

3045. The upper torso of a statue of a god, probably seated, of over life size. The himation leaves bare the right part of the body. The work of some Ionian (Parian?) artist about 500 B.C. Provenance unknown. Height 0.90 m.

4468. Part of a poros metope, heavy. There is preserved the lower body of a goddess, seated full face, dressed in chiton, and cloaked also with himation. She supports her feet on a high flat stool. A fine late archaic work about 490 B.C. with careful attention to the rendering of the folds. Found at Megara in 1954. Height 0.44 m., width 0.37 m., depth 0.277 m.

3897. Torso of a colossal statue of Dionysos. Holes above the chest for the fixing of the locks. The folds of the chiton and of the himation without much elevation. The formation plane at the sides and back. Found in 1888 at Dionysos (Ikaria) in Attica. Brought to the Museum in 1942. Height 0.60 m., width 0.60 m.

To this statue probably belongs the base with two feet no. **3074**, as well as the right hand with the kantharos no. **3073**.

3851. Sepulchral statue of a Kouros, Kroisos, above a base of three steps. The arms separated from the body, the hair falls at the back in a curve, rounding toward the sides. On the central step, the only ancient one, is carved the inscription: « Stop (traveller) and mourn near the monument of the dead Kroisos whom the raging Ares destroyed when one day he fought among the defenders ». Found at Anavyssos in Attica in 1936. The inscribed step was gi-

ven to the Museum in 1954 by a foreign friend of antiquities. Radiant, monumental sculpture of about 520 B.C.
Height 1.94 m.

1926. A pair of jumping weights of archaic type, of
hard stone. Found at Corinth. The fingers would have
passed through the hole. End of the 6th century or the
beginning of the 5th B.C. Width 0.23 - 0.24 m.

2569. Statuette of a goddess seated on a simple chair
with foot stool. She wears an Ionian chiton and himation.
A large opening for the insertion of the head. Found at
Rhamnous. Reverent delicate Attic work of the advanced
archaic period, about 520 B.C. Height 0.45 m.

3892. The lower part of an Attic grave stele. Two young
men nude facing right, one holding a spear. Fine Attic
art of about 500 B.C. Found at Laurion. It has been known
since 1887. Height 0.72 m.

89, 2823, 2826. Relief plaques probably for the invest-
ment of a grave monument. On the two first Hermes as conductor of souls, on the third the feet of the deceased. About
500 B.C. Found in the Kerameikos. They had been ham-
mered for their insertion in the Themistoclean Wall, in 478
B.C. Height of the better preserved 0.87 m.

1772. Fragment of a relief plaque. The head of an athlete
is discerned (his hand above which hurls the javelin). About
540 B.C. Found in the cemetery of the Kerameikos in 1906
(compare also the adjacent plaques 89, 2823, 2826). Height
0.275 m.

42 and **3579.** Square base (for a small statue of Herakles?) with deep reliefs on three sides. On two the struggle
with the Nemean lion and the capture of the two headed Cerberus from Hades. On the third Heràkles relaxes stretched
out on the ground. It was found in the village of Lamprika

(ancient Lamptrai) in Attica. End of the 6th century B. C. Height 0.19 m., width 0.49 m., of the narrow undecorated side 0.36 m.

796. Double palmette with separated spirals and petals, with delicate carving. Attic work with Ionian influence, probably the upper shaft of a funeral stele. Provenance unknown. About 440 B.C. Height 0.59 m.

40. The upper shaft of a grave stele, with double relief. It lacks the palmette which crowned it. Delicate relief, the head of a young man facing right. Found in the ancient Dikaia of Thracian Abdera in 1858. On the lower shaft of the stele (in the Museum of Komotini, found in 1927) is preserved the body of the young man wrapped in his himation. On the back the figure of his young servant, and his dog. Delicate Ionian work about 500 B. C. Height 0.49 m., length 0.39 m.

3476. Square base for a statue of a Kouros with reliefs on three sides. A. In the centre two young men (epheboi) wrestle, nude with their hands engaged. On the right a similar youth is incising on the ground a dividing line with a long javelin. On the left another is preparing to jump. B. The left adjacent side: six nude athletes. The last one on the left is preparing to throw a ball. The near one and the two last on the right with lively gestures seem to take part in the game. The two central confronting athletes are runners (the one, the runner of a « stade », the other with the clenched hands, long distance runner). The composition, symmetrical, has however antithetical details in the poses, the movement concentrates on the four border figures. A replica of this representation is preserved in the principal scene of a base of the Museum of the Kerameikos, a little older. An important work would be used as a prototype for the two. C. Graceful scene of four athletes in relaxation after their exercises. The two central seated figures are playing, inciting a dog and a cat to fight. Two companions stand behind them, all wearing the himation. The large vacant space between the seated figures, all red, helps to show them. A little better preserved is the colour of the background on the other side panel. The arrangement of these radiant, smiling young figures, the anatomical details, the treatment of folds, recall the best vase paintings of Euphronios at the time of Kleisthenes (about 510 B.C.) The base would have stood on a narrow under base. Found in 1922 built into the Themistoclean Wall of the Kerameikos. See the adjacent one no. 3477. Height 0.29 m., width 0.79 m. (The same on all sides). (Pl. 16 a-b).

3477. Base of a statue of an archaic Kouros. There are reliefs on three sides, on two a procession of four-horse chariots and hoplites. On the central panel four young athletes playing hockey. Red colour on the rim of the shields on the inner side. The reliefs in addition to their thin plastic elevation would have been emphasized with colours. About 490 B.C. Found in 1922 in the Kerameikos together with no. 3476, built into the Themistoclean Wall of 478 B.C. Below as is 3476. Height 0.28 m., width 0.60 m. of the narrow sides; of the principal panel 0.82 m.

4488. The upper part of the face of a statue of a Kouros. The locks of hair, held back by a narrow band, cover the forehead to its lower edge. The compressed lips fleshy, the carving careless. End of the 6th century B.C. Unknown provenance. Height 0.13 m.

36. Part of a votive or grave relief. Two women confronted, the left seated in the manner of heroized figures. A fine late archaic Attic work, about 500 B.C. Provenance unknown. Height 0.43 m.

3936. Torso of a statue of Victory (?) running toward the right with the left leg bent. She wears a chiton and himation. Her hair falls obliquely at the back. Late archaic. It was probably an acroterion of some temple. Found in Athens east of the Tower of the Winds in 1933. Height 0.60 m., width 0.53 m.

3344. The upper part of a relief probably votive. A nude young man facing left crowns his own head, which is surrounded with a light band. Below this are holes for the attachment of a metal crown. The hair falls short at the back above the neck. On the left traces of the blue colour which covered the plaque, background of the figure. Marvellous Attic creation of early classical style. About 460 B.C. It still has strong plastic formation, level at certain points, and a spiritual expression. Found in 1915 at Sounion, near the temple of Athena. Height 0.48 m., width 0.495 m. (Pl. 18).

3990. Round plaque in relief, concave, on the outer surface, carving toward the centre. On the left part is the head of a goddess facing right. All the hair at the back covered with a net. A hole in front of the ears held the fastening (probably gold) which adorned the hair. The lips open and full, the chin strong, the nose prominent. Aphrodite is here the goddess of spring and rebirth. In the empty part of the plaque there would have been a plant. A wonderful work of a Parian (?) sculptor, representative of the severe style in its island rendering. 470-460 B. C. Found on Melos in 1936. Height 0.32 m., width 0.36 m. Depth at the centre 0.075 m., at the edge 0.015 m. (Pl. 17).

733. Grave stele of Polyxena (the name engraved on the left side : *I am Polyxenaia*). It ends above with a simple pediment with acroteria. Found at Larisa. A somewhat unskillful work of a local sculptor, with archaic reverence. About 440 B.C. Height 1.10 - 1.12 m.

734. Grave monument of Ekkedamos, with simple round pediment (his name carved perpendicularly on the right). The young man, standing, holds in his left hand two spears, in his right a cock. Found at Larisa in 1882. Rough but expressive work by a local sculptor, about 440 B.C. with archaic stiffness. Height 1.28 m.

740. Grave stele, with frame (formerly crowned by a palmette?). The upper part with the head of the figure is missing. A woman facing left standing in front of a low stool, with right leg bent, holds a hare above her left arm. Found in 1883 in Thessaly, far from Larisa. A Thessalian work, rough but individual and austere with an attempt at rendering the planes. About 440 B.C. Height 1.25 m., width 0.62 m.

741. Grave stele, large and heavy, rectangular. It ends above in a palmette with hollow petals. A young man standing, facing right, with short chiton and with chlamys, the petasos on his head, holds in his right hand a hare and in the other a fruit. The lower part of the stele was found at Larisa in 1881, the upper part a few kilometres beyond in 1887. One of the best Thessalian grave stelai, full of funereal reverence. About the middle of the 5th century B.C. Total height 2.46 m., height of the relief 1.56 m.

4475. Fragment of a grave stele. On the right the upper nude body of a man, bald. He is seated on a chair facing left and holds a sceptre, lifting his head toward a confronting figure, missing, to whom he offers his right hand. Found at Pharsala in 1955. Rough but expressive, a typical Thessalian work of the second half of the 5th century B.C. Height 0.43 m., width 0.44 m.

735. Grave stele of a man, rhapsodist (?). Upright, he steps toward the right with his head slightly inclined; he accompanies with singing the playing of the lyre which he holds. About 460 B. C. Found in Vonitsa in Akarnania in 1891. A somewhat clumsy but fresh work of a local sculptor with Ionian influence. Height 1.88 m.

739. Grave stele of Amphotto with simple pediment. She is standing, dressed in a simple girded peplos. Her hair falls abundantly above her back, a polos on her head. Her name is engraved in front of her face. Found in 1890 in the village of Pyri near Thebes. Work of a Boeotian sculptor, simple but reverent, it gives sanctity to the figure of the dead girl. About 440 B.C. Height 0.81 m. (Pl. 19).

3205. The left lower part of a large grave stele. A dog seated on his hind legs, facing left, raises his head to the right toward his master; only the lower right leg of the latter is preserved. Found on Anaphe. Strong, full the plastic structure. Probably by a Parian sculptor, about 460 - 450 B.C. Height 0.66 m.

39. Grave stele of a man. The finial is lacking. He supports himself with a staff in his left hand while with the other he offers a grasshopper to his dog. Carved inscription : « *Alxenor the Naxian made me. Just look !* » (the stele speaks). Found at Orchomenos in Boeotia in 1860. Rough work of a local stone of a Boeotian marble worker, an imitation of a charming Ionian prototype. Beginning of the 5th century B.C. Height 1.97 m., width 0.61 - 0.62 m.

4478. Large Ionic capital with two spirals (the one on the left missing), in the centre a circular plastic swelling. On the upper edges there is relief decoration and lower decoration painted in black. Similar ornaments drawn on the protuberance between the spirals. Fine example of early classical Ionic capital of Attica. From the second temple of Athena at Sounion. Length 0.68-0.69 m., depth 0.58 - 0.59 m., height 0.40 m.

4479. Similar to no. 4478, better preserved, but the colours effaced. Below the spirals is preserved the hollow cavity. Found with the preceding example. Length 0.875 m., depth 0.58 m., height 0.411 m.

44. Fragment of a grave stele with narrow surrounding frame. The upper body of a bearded man facing right, with himation (the right arm bare). Found on Kythnos. Delicate island work of about 470 B.C. Height 0.41 m., width 0.27 m.

126. Large Eleusinian relief. The three figures stand on a horizontal projection. On the left Demeter holds the sceptre in her raised right hand, in the fingers of the other the sacred grain which she proffers to the young man facing her, Triptolemos. In front of the scene, nude, he holds back with his left hand the edge of his himation, with the other he accepts from the goddess the gift which is to save mankind when he traverses the earth, the cultivation of the grain. Standing behind him, Kore (Persephone), holds a large torch loosely, while bending her head she gives her blessing to the young man with her right hand above his head. The figures of the two goddesses in their elevation recall cult statues, that of Triptolemos is inspired from Ionian works. The grain would have been gold, Triptolemos would have worn a gold crown. The whole severe composition conservative in the style (the figure of Demeter with its flat perpendicular pleats of the peplos) offsets the later details (the graceful figure of Kore). A local sculptor's work which, restricted by the Eleusinian worship, gives the mysterious religious grandeur which permeates the scene, the poses, the gestures, the faces. The relief would probably have been placed within the Telesterion of Eleusis, found, however, in the lower town in 1859. A copy of the Roman period in the Metropolitan Museum. Height 2.20 m. (Pl. 20).

828. Grave stele of a horseman, heavy, of local stone. The horse gallops toward the right. The chlamys of the horseman is blown out behind. Harness of metal was inserted on the throat and the mouth of the horse (holes). Probably a grave stele as an offering for a holy man, a hero. The upper part with the head of the horseman is missing.

Found at Thespiae in 1814. Fine work of a Boeotian sculptor about 430 B.C. Height 1.20 m., width 1.03 m.

1385. Large relief plaque, simple, with a horse, the horseman standing behind it facing left. On his arm are holes for the fixing of the metal spear, another for the reins. Simple but skillful rendering of the horse. The lower part is missing, the heads broken. From the older acquisitions, formerly in the Museum of Aegina and it seems probable it was found there. It is uncertain whether it would have been votive or sepulchral (Ephemeris of the Government 1829, p. 259). Height of the ancient part 0.79 m., width 0.96 m.

96. The front part of the head of a bearded god, from a mask, probably of Dionysos or from a Hermaic stele. A light band around the head. Fine Attic art of traditional archaic style, about 470 B. C. Found on the south slopes of the Acropolis in 1876. Height 0.23 m.

2337. Small head of a bearded Zeus (?). A band around the head. The hair gathered together falls to the neck. The rendering of the beard schematic and linear. Late archaic, about 480 B.C. Found at Rhamnous. Height 0.11 m.

1949. Small head of a young man facing right, fragment of a relief. The hair held together with a light double band covers his forehead. Locks of hair fall in waves in front of his ear. A radiant, sculptured work of the early classical period (about 460 B.C.). Found on the south slopes of the Acropolis (Wall of the Serpentze). Height 0.14 m. (P l. 21 b).

1848. Statue of a goddess, headless. Clothed in a peplos girded and with a fold. The himation covers the back of the body hanging low effecting a considerable motionless depth. A charming Attic work of the early classic period. Found at Rhamnous in 1890. Height 0.43 m. (P l. 21 a).

381. Head of a young woman with her hair rolled up in a snood. Only the locks, somewhat loose, emerge above at her temples. Fine Attic work of the early classical period, about 450 B.C. The whole statue would have been an acroterion of some Athenian temple. Provenance unknown. Height 0.25 m.

4516. The upper body of a small statue of a bearded man, probably a Centaur. He had raised his arms aggressively. It comes perhaps from a metope or pediment of an Athenian temple. Very good Attic work of about 450 B.C. with late archaic accuracy in the rendering of the beard. It lacks the upper part of the head. Provenance unknown. Height 0.18 m.

1763. Head of Athena with large Corinthian helmet high on her head and plain at the back. The hair appears on the forehead, more at the temples and the neck. Plain, nice work, probably Attic of the early classical style about 450 B.C. The lips and the nose are missing. Battered. Provenance unknown. Height 0.28 m., length of the helmet 0.25 m.

85. Ionic capital. The scrolls rhythmically curved, with delicate carving from both views. Square hollow for the reception of the plinth with dedication, a statue standing or seated. One of the finest Ionic capitals of the early Attic type. From the Varvakeion collection. The whole work would have been placed on the Acropolis, as others like it. Height 0.22 m., width 0.45 m.

742. Large rectangular stele of a young man. A disk in relief for the front of the central acroterion. In the foreground of the plaque below, a nude youth stands firmly on both feet, the left leg slightly advanced and bent. In his right hand he holds his chlamys which falls at the shoulders, in his left hand a stlengis and a purse. Standing in front of

his feet in low relief is his dog. The inscription: « 'Αγαθοκλῆ
χαῖρε » from the second use of the stele in the Hellenistic
period. Found at Thespiae in 1884. Work of a local sculptor
in hard Boeotian stone influenced by a good Ionian prototype. About 440 B.C. Height 2.24 m., width about 0.78 m.

54. Small square altar with relief on three sides. Above
on the curved terminal a relief of palmettes and lotus flowers.
A. Hermes, nude, bearded, facing right holds a ram on
his shoulder, wearing a chlamys, the herald's staff in his
hand. B. The upper body of Aphrodite (?) facing right (her
head turned to the left) with diaphanous chiton. The back
panel is not well finished. It seems probable that with its
second use, as well as the hollowing of the surface above,
the figures of the third side would have been scraped away.
Delicate style, archaistic, of the second half of the 5th
century B.C. Found in Athens about 1850. Height 0.44 m.,
width 0.26 m.

1732. Statue of a young woman, flying (lacking the
wings). The lower body is designed with a harmonious diagonally curve, the upper presses forward. Below the Attic
peplos which, girded low, outlines her youthful body, while
the right part of her beautiful breast is bared. A pleasing
work of the classical style about 440 B.C. It was probably
a central acroterion of the temple of Ares and perhaps represented Hebe, if not a Breeze of Attica. Found near the
Theseion in 1891. The fragment of the left leg was found in
1951. Height 0.98 m. (Pl. 22).

Br. 15161. The Poseidon of Artemision. Large bronze
statue of a god. It was found on the ocean bed off Artemision (North Euboea) by divers, first the arm in 1926 and
then in 1928 the statue. Poseidon is represented as bran-
dishing the trident ; the horizontal line from this would
go past his face (the open fingers preclude the possibility

of his holding the flaming thunderbolt, it is not therefore a statue of Zeus as formerly suggested). The braid of hair around the head, charming locks of hair above the narrow forehead. A work full of spirit of one of the principal bronze workers of the North Peloponnese in the early classical period, probably of Kalamis. His achievement was that by a process inherited from the archaic period he created an internal freedom and the power of a new sense of movement, in the face an unprecedented divine expression. About 450 B.C. (Pl. 23).

1738. Head of a woman with a peculiar type of helmet which resembles a lionskin. The hair visible only on the forehead, the eyes almond-shaped. It comes from the doorway of a monument and probably represented Omphale who allured Herakles. Found in Lycia. Local work of about 440 B.C. Height 0.25 m.

1825. Small rectangular relief stele, of poros with a surrounding frame and with a square base. A nude boy, standing, facing left, holds a staff in his left hand, in his right something like a flower. The body undeveloped, flabby, with a disproportionate height in the upper part. Abundant traces of red in the background, and likewise on the hair. Found in Lycia ; it would have been on the entrance of a tomb carved in the rock. Local work. Height 1.10 m., width of the stele 0.30 m.

43. Votive relief with simple pediment. Herakles, facing right, had lifted on his left shoulder the Erymanthian boar with the head down and th efeet high. Found in Athens, near the Theseion, in 1839. Beginning of the 5th century B.C. Height 0.76 m.

332. Head of a bearded god, Zeus or Hermes, from a Hermaic stele. The rich locks of hair cover the temples also, the rest of the hair with a band around the head falls bellow as far as the neck. Found in 1866 at Piraeus in an ancient sanctuary of Hetonia. According to one opinion it is the work of the Parian sculptor Euphron, who had signed a Hermes of the same find. About 440 B.C. Height 0.31 m.

3850. Head of a bearded god with encircling band. It belongs to an Hermaic stele. Above the forehead a hole for the attachment of a metal « horn » (κέρας). Good Attic work with influence of Parthenonian figures. Found in Attica. Brought to the National Museum in 1938. About 430 B.C. Height 0.17 m.

648. Large head of a woman from a « peplos wearing » statue (dressed in the Doric peplos). Copy of the Roman period of a famous bronze original, work of some Peloponnesian sculptor, about 460 B.C. Provenance unknown. Height 0.33 - 0.34 m.

127. Marble krater unfinished (« Finley Krater » because it belonged to the collection of the English historian). The relief copies the famous work of Myron placed on the Acropolis (460-450 B.C.). Athena throws away the flutes because they disfigured the face of the flute player. The satyr Marsyas rushes to take them. Neo-Attic work of the first century B.C. It lacks the whole base. Height 0.46 m., diam. above 0,42 m. It was found in Athens.

229. The lower part of a group of Athena struggling with the giant Enkelados. The base rounded on the left side. The goddess rushes towards the right; under her legs is the right leg of the fallen giant. In front of her is his bent left leg. Carefully worked also from the back but of cold classicizing workmanship. Found at Laurion in 1887. Probably of the first or the beginning of the second century A.D. Height 0.44 m., length 0.95 m.

1664 - 1664 a. Two torsos of statues of Theseus and the Minotaur. The first headless, the head of the Minotaur has an inclination toward the left. A deep hole under the mouth of the Minotaur shows that the head had been used as a fountain. Both are copies of a classical sculpture composition. Theseus raised his sword above the Minotaur. Found in Athens. Height of Theseus 0.82 m., of the Minotaur 0.73 m.

45. The « Apollo of the Omphalos ». The statue owes this modern name to the adjacent omphalos no. 46 which was found with it in the theatre of Dionysos in 1862. The god, nude, rests his weight on the right leg. The locks of hair fall low on his forehead, a plait around the hair. Of the 2nd century A.D., a good copy of a well known bronze original of about 450 B.C. which is considered the work of a great artist of the early classical period and specifically of Kalamis. The same artist seems to have been the creator of the large bronze Poseidon from Artemision. An addition by the copyist is the support which can be discerned above the left leg of Apollo. Height 1.76 m. (Pl. 24).

46. Base of a statue in the form of an omphalos which broadens at the bottom. « Emblems » in relief with diagonal arrangement and with two successive planes. On the upper, the formerly smooth surface, and at the edge is preserved the sole with the toes of the right foot of a statue of Apollo. On the other edge traces of the left foot. Found in 1862 in the theatre of Dionysos. It does not, however, belong to the adjacent no. 45. Height 0.70 m., diam. of the upper circle 0.47 m.

3020. Head of a statue of Apollo. Around the head a light band. Above the narrow forehead the locks of hair are bound around, braid at the back between the ears. A mediocre copy of the first century A.D. of a good bronze creation of the early classical technique. About 450 B.C. Found in Athens in 1910. Height 0.20 m.

3775. Small head of a youth facing right, from a relief. Possibly from a three-figure relief (with a representation of Orpheus and Eurydice?). It is a copy of the first century A.D. Found in the excavations of the ancient Academy in 1933. Height 0.16 m.

248. Statue of a nude youth. He stands on the soles of both feet with the left knee bent. The locks of hair schematic, archaistic, around his head. It is uncertain what he held in his left hand. Probably an eclectic work of the second century A.D. without rhythm in the body. Found in the Olympeion in Athens in 1888. Height 1.25 m.

In this room have been placed all the Attic grave stelai of the 5th century B.C.

About 500 B. C. after a prohibitory law the custom of erecting grave stelai in Athens ceased. Only after 440 B.C. do Attic stelai of the classical period begin again. The first examples are narrow with 1 – 2 figures in a fairly high relief. The expression of the faces, takes on slowly the unspoken grief which characterizes the Attic stele of the classical period.

Toward the end of the 5th century the stele changes its form, the shrine with pediment, and becomes carved with more elevation ; about 400 B.C. appears the three - figure composition, with the one seated figure. The quest for a monumental quality, apparent in these works, will take, in the coming century, a broader extent and a more communal content. The stelai of the fifth century have, however, a deep spiritual expression and an individual restrained beauty.

3947. Grave stele oblong, with pediment. On the left a man wearing a himation gives a bird to a youth. On the epistyle are the names: *Philokles* son of *Dikaios, Dikaios* son of *Philokles* (father and young son). It is one of the oldest Attic stelai of the 5th century with the relief still low and without a frame. Good post-Parthenon carving. About 430 B.C. Found at Chalandri in Attica about 1958. Height with the restored central acroterion: 0.93 m., width below 0.42 m.

712. Grave stele of the Iphistiades, with pediment (where there is a relief of two antithetic lions). On the stele two men standing in a welcoming scene, behind on the left a woman. Above the epistyle are carved the names of three men of the family of the Iphistiades as well as the name of Timariste. Found in Athens in 1853. One of the earliest Attic stelai of the fifth century, about 440 B. C. Height of the relief 0.94 m. Together with the lower smooth part 1.12 m.

880. Grave stele, oblong, with rounded pediment (relief of flower and two facing animals). The representation is in slight relief. Two men wearing the himation offer their hands in welcome. Between them a girl raises her hand and her head toward the man on the right. It was in the Museum of Piraeus until 1888. It is one of the oldest Attic stelai of the 5th century B.C. 440-430 B.C. Height 1.08 m.

713. Small grave stele with a figure in relief. A woman is seated on a high throne facing left. She holds in her left hand an egg or a bird, in her right hand a phiale. A pediment is sketched above in relief. Found in Piraeus. It would be the oldest known Attic stele of the 5th century if its technique did not relate it closely to Thessalian stelai. According to one opinion it is the work of some Thessalian sculptor placed on the tomb of a compatriot. About 450 B.C. Height 1.05 m.

766. Grave stele of the little Aristylla, with pediment. Standing on the right Aristylla holds a bird in her left hand and with the other greets her mother who is seated on a chair. The inscription, engraved on the projection below the figures, is : « *Here lies Aristylla, the wise daughter of Ariston and Rodille* ». It is one of the simple, serious, early Attic stelai of the 5th century. 440-430 B.C. Found in Piraeus. Height 0.87 m., width below 0.44 m.

716. Part of a grave stele in the form of a shrine. The left half of the face of a seated woman who holds a pyxis. Facing her and looking at her are two figures, a woman and a bearded man who extends his lowered right hand. Found in Piraeus in 1837. Fine Attic work of about 420 B.C. with influence of the frieze of the Parthenon. Height 1.44 m.

1680. Part of the grave stele of Aristomache. It had the form of a shrine. There is preserved in slight relief the lower body of a young woman to the left with a windblown himation.

Her name is in the inscription below her feet. An excellent work of about 410 B.C. showing influence of the work of Agorakritos. Found in Athens in 1891. Height 0.71 m., width 0.47 m.

4502. The square base of a marble lekythos or loutrophoros with moulding and epistyle. It has relief decoration on three sides. A. The Elysian fields (?). On the principal side a young woman (the deceased) received in her lap the apples which the young man opposite to her gathers from a tree. B. Hermes as guide of souls wears a short chiton, chlamys and petasos and carries the herald's staff (once, painted). A priest, with full length, ungirt chiton, aquiline holds the long sacrificial knife. Splendid Attic work with super-terrestrial symbolism. End of the 5th century B. C. Found in Athens (1958). Height 0.83 m., width of A. 0.50 m., width of the adjoining sides 0.31 m.

4485. Large marble funeral lekythos of Myrrhine. The part above the neck is missing, as well as the lower part with the base. On the centre Hermes as guide of souls, clothed in the chlamys, with one foot winged leads a young woman, holding her by the hand, to the left toward the river Acheron. Myrrhine (the name is carved above her bent head) wears a chiton and the himation covers her head as well. On the left three relatives look at the scene, the last one resting his elbow on a pillar closes the composition. Found in Athens (Constitution Square) in 1873. Brought to the Museum in 1960. Though one of the nobler Attic monuments this lekythos does not, even so, seem to be the work of an important sculptor. About 420 B.C. Height of the ancient part 1.36 m.

37. Fragment of a grave stele with relief figure. The upper body of a nude young man facing left, with bent head lowered left arm. The pose is uncertain. Found on Kythnos.

Delicate work of an island sculptor about 430 B.C. Height 0.62 m., width 0.37 m.

3254. The upper part of a small grave stele. A little girl facing left holds in her right hand probably a small bird. A nice work with somewhat crude carving. About 430 B.C. Found in Athens. Height 0.32 m., width 0.35 m.

713. Grave stele of Chairestrate and Lysander, of the early type with relief pediment. Chairestrate standing facing right gives a bird to the youth Lysander. The names are carved above their heads. About 430 B.C. Found in Athens. Height 0.90 m., width about 0.44 m.

3845. Grave stele of Mnesagora and her little brother, Nikochares, with plain moulding and epistyle. On the left the little girl bends affectionately toward the small nude boy, who rises offering a bird. According to the four - line epigram carved on the epistyle the parents erected the stele to their two dead children. From Anagyrous (Vari) in Attica. It was in the Petraki monastery (Athens)until 1927. It is one of the earliest Attic stelai of the 5th century with simple moving tenderness. About 440. B.C. Height 1.19 m., width 0.74 m.

910. Fragment of an Attic stele. There is preserved the body of a girl facing right with chiton and himation, with plain hairdress. She holds in her two hands a pyxis. Work of nobility in a somewhat archaic manner. Wavy lines are visible on the hair. About 440 B.C. Found in Athens in 1883. Height 0.48 m., width 0.33 m.

4470. Fragment of a grave stele. On the right the upper body of a young man who bends over a seated figure. Only her hand is preserved which holds a tablet (?). A tender work of an island sculptor about 420 B.C. Found on Amorgos. Height 0.38 m.

715. The upper part of a grave stele with cornice and a marked horizontal projection. It has a relief band of palmettes and lotus flowers. A young man, frontal, with himation on his lower body holds a bird in his left hand and raises the other in front of a hanging cage. Lower, above a stele a cat is seated. A small servant, standing, nude, in front of the stele, with grief suffusing his childish face, would be holding the athletic equipment of his master. A radiant work of an important sculptor (Agorakritos?) who worked on the Parthenon frieze. About 430 B.C. Found on Salamis (or in one opinion on Aegina). It was in the Aegina Museum in the time of Capodistria. Height 1.04 m., width 0.81 m. (Pl. 25).

2670. The left section of a large grave stele in the form of a shrine. In a quite elaborate relief a girl standing, facing right, gazes at a mirror which she holds in her left hand. The ends of her hair at the back in a thick cluster. One of the more charming stelai of about 410 B.C. Found in Attica about 1905. Height 0.95 m., width 0.63 m.

3379. Attic stele with pediment (but no side pieces) and a three-figure relief, fairly tender. A hoplite, facing right, and two women, the second shorter. Found in Attica in 1916. Fine archaic work of a sculptor with Ionian influence. About 430 B.C. Height 1.43 m., width 0.98 m.

1858. Fragment of a grave stele of a young woman, with horizontal moulding. On the left the upper body of a servant with Argive peplos. She holds in her hands open a pyxis with jewels. Found in Athens. In the National Museum since 1900. It is a work very closely related (by the same sculptor ?) to the beautiful stele of the young man, no. 715. About 420 B.C. Height 0.67 m., width above 0.54 m.

2588. Small stele of the sailor Eudemides of Torone. There is a band under the name, formerly painted, which extends also to the two narrow sides. In ancient times the marble of the stele was the marble tile of some building. Beginning of the 4th century B.C. Found at Aghia Triada (Athens). Height 0.42 m.

2592. The upper part of a small stele (from a child's tomb?) with a floral roof. Inscription: Aristippos of Lampsacus. Two painted bands on the epistyle. Found near the Kerameikos. Height 0.31 m.

2611. A small stele placed on the tomb of a Scythian. The painted quiver is preserved. Below is the inscription: Aristomedes placed this. Known since 1884. Found in Athens, west of the Kerameikos. Whole height (with the unworked base) : 0.69 m., width 0.195 m.

714. Grave stele, formerly in the form of a shrine. On the left a seated woman welcomes a young woman standing facing her. Toward the latter a bearded man gazes with deep sorrow. It is, however, uncertain which of the two women is the deceased. Beautiful Attic work, transitional to the elaborate funeral stele of the 4th century and the balanced three-figure composition. About 390 B.C. Found possibly at Piraeus. Height 1.24 m., width 0.70 m.

1929. Small grave stele, simple and delicate. It is fastened with lead to the unworked heavy poros base. On the front surface a red band tied together in a knot. Above the name of the deceased: Hediste. Found in the Kerameikos (1891). Height of the stele 0.51 m., width about 0.30 m., height of the base 0.185 m., width 0.41 m.

3709. Grave stele, simple, with a double relief on the upper part (two sculptures). A. Lion, B. Lioness. On the bare surface below there would have been painted a figure or funeral bands. About 430 B.C. Found in the Kerameikos (1930). Height 1.13 m., width about 0.47 m.

ROOM OF CLASSICAL VOTIVE SCULPTURE

Between the two rooms of the grave monuments of the 5th century there exists another free from the shadow of death. There have been placed as in the small adjacent rooms only those votive to the gods, small or large reliefs and statues, as well as architectural members from ancient temples : metopes from the Argive Heraion, small heads of warriors from the sculptured decoration of the temple, besides fragments of the floral sima, and small charming remains from the sculptured base of the statue of Nemesis at Rhamnous.

The votive reliefs of the room are among the most important, the most radiant examples of the 5th century. Otherwise this class carved by simple marbleworkers with unskilful hands, but with a sensitive feeling, belongs to the people. Those selected for these rooms are works of practised sculptors ; some many figured have original scenes, studied compositions. The sky - blue colour of the background would have helped to display the figures.

The ancient sacred precincts, the stoai, the outdoor areas, the propylaia of the temples were filled with these reliefs. The pious pilgrims would have placed them also in separate little shrines or caves. The deeply rooted, reflective piety of the Greeks, together with another permanent expression of their life, their art, is apparent in the votive reliefs. They loose something in the fatal isolation of the Museum, they gain living qualities, if one imagines them in their ancient settings, bathed in light, sanctified by the presence of gods and heroes, gaining beauty from the worship of the faithful. The ardent and devout worshippers saw somewhere close at hand the representation of the same god which prepared them for the « appearance » (Epiphany). The thrill of such visions is diffused into various figures of gods which the sculptors and artists have carved from the marble.

3278. Part of a votive relief. A nude young man facing left, standing in front of a horse. Attic work with echoes of Parthenon style. About 430 B.C. Found on Kythera in 1912. Height 0.42 m.

1783. Votive relief, double, with pediment and akroterion. Above, with four horse chariot the hero Echelos and the nymph Vasile. In front Hermes leading the nymph, with the whip in his right hand (formerly painted). The ground, uneven, rises below the god in the form of a rock. Traces of blue in the background of the relief. On the epistyle are carved the names of the figures. On the B panel on the left Artemis (?) confronted by a god. In the centre the river god Kephisos, horned, facing the spectator, three nymphs following. The central figure is inspired by the type of the Aphrodite «Fréjus» (called also Louvre - Naples). The composition is more condensed on this side, the right. On the epistyle is carved «Hermes and the Nymphs». Found in 1903 in New Phaleron, in the same shrine as the relief of Xenokrateia, no. 2756. In the deme of the Echelides was the large hippodrome of the Athenians. In addition to the heroes of the underworld, Echelos and Vasile, Kephisos would have been worshipped also in the shrine. The heavy poros bases of the two reliefs have been set up in the room of the altar. This wonderful, most important Attic relief is dated about 410 B.C. Height with the central acroterion: 0.75 m., width 0.88 m. (P l. 27).

468. Head of an ephebos (young man), from a statue or from a Hermaic stele. A band around the head, with the hair short. Good Attic original work of the school of Agorakritos. About 430 B.C. Found in Athens. Height 0.20-0.21 m.

199. Statue of a young man wearing a himation, with its base (the latter of dark-coloured marble). According to the inscription carved on the base it was the dedication of Lysikleides, son of Epandrides. Attic work, somewhat provincial but charming, of the school of Agorakritos, about 420 B.C. The head, turned toward the side of the stationary leg, maintains the classical balance. Found in 1890 at Rhamnous in Attica in the temple of Themis. Total height 1.96 m., height of the statue 0.02 m.

In the show case :

Fragments of small carved figures in deep relief from the base of the goddess Nemesis at Rhamnous in Attica. The subject was the presentation of Helen by her substitute mother Leda, to her real mother Nemesis, for her marriage with Menelaos. They were all found near the great temple, in the excavations of 1890. The individuality which characterizes the statue of the goddess Nemesis by the˝ Pheidian pupil Agorakritos, can be distinguished in the balanced yet free classical pose of the figures, the expression of the faces, the carving of the marble which has spirit and lifes, as well as exceptional quality. About 420 B.C.

211-212. Bodies of two male statues, clad in the himation.

213. Lower body of a woman wearing a peplos. To this probably belongs the upper body no. **209.** It probably represents Nemesis in a severe matriarchal pose.

208. Body of a young woman with diaphanous chiton and himation. To this belongs the head no. **203** with its stern beauty. It is the beautiful maiden Helen. (P l. 29 a).

205-206. Two heads of youths, the first somewhat square. They have the « blissful sorrow » of the Parthenon frieze. Dioskouroi ?

207. Head of a horse, possibly of one of the Dioskouroi (the side part of the base).

2348. Fragment of a large sculpture, with irregular plinth, in the form of a rock. There is preserved the lower right leg of a woman, wrapped in the folds of a « Lakonian » peplos. Only a trace is preserved of the sole of the left foot at a suitable distance from the other. Higher is the foot and part of the calf of a man who ran to approach the maiden: Boreas and Oreithyia. Found at Rhamnous in Attica. The group composed the central acroterion of the later temple of Nemesis at Rhamnous. Marvellous, probably by the hand of Agorakritos, pupil of Pheidias, with the inspired carving of the marble and the vitality of the north wind (Boreas) Total height 0.51 m., width 0.72 m. Maximum height of the plinth at the back 0.16 m.

1500. Votive relief, simple, without architectural formation. On the right Dionysos, stretched on a bed facing left, holds a rhyton in his right hand, and in the other a phiale. On the edge of the bed is seated a young, graceful woman with her face turned back toward the male figure whom she « worships » with the right hand, holding a mask in her lowered left hand. At the back a pair of two other confronted men. The first holds a drum and a tragic mask, the other a drum in his raised hand (the head formerly attached is missing). The remains of an inscription below the figures from the second use of the work. It was a dedication to Dionysos by ancient actors who are represented in the Dionysiac costume (sleeved chiton long and girded peplos over it). The masks and drums suggest the hypothesis that it was dedicated to the god after a performance of the « Bacchae » of Euripides. The seated female figure would be symbolic. An illuminating Attic work about 410 B.C., also an important monument of the archaic theatre. Found in Piraeus. Height 0.55 m., width 0.93 m.

1391. Part of a votive relief. There is preserved the back part of a two wheeled vehicle, the charioteer in the chariot. By his side a young hoplite, nude, the apobates, leaps from the chariot, holding his shield. On the epistyle traces of an inscription. Good work, about 400 B.C. Found in the Amphiareion near Oropos in 1887. Height 0.60 m., width 0.38 m.

3410. A small statue, headless, of a seated goddess, from Sounion. About 430 B.C. Height 0.58 m., length 0.45 m.

1112. Acroterion of the west pediment of the temple of Poseidon at Sounion. From high spirals toward the summit a palmette sprouts with classic simplicity, in relief without much elevation. Found at Sounion. About 440 B.C. One of the early classical examples of this kind. Height of the ancient part 0.14 m.

1394. Part of a votive relief. An ephebos, wearing a chlamys, standing, facing right, toward two horses of a chariot of which he holds the reins. 430-420 B.C., with influence of the Parthenon frieze. Unknown provenance. Height 0.56 m., width 0.41 m.

3076. Fragment of a small, simple votive relief. On the left, seated on a chair with high support a goddess facing right, dressed in Ionic sleeved chiton. She holds out the phiale with her right hand, raising in her other hand the edge of the himation which also covers her lower body. Her hair would have been coloured. Delicate style, post - Parthenonian. About 420 B.C. Found at Ikaria in Attica (Dionysos).

3941. Corner of a frieze. From the decorative relief a warrior is distinguished facing right who, stooping slightly, confronts an adversary. Found in the bed of the Ilissos in 1894, it belongs to the frieze of the little temple of the Ilissos. Known from plans of the 18th century this delicate Ionic temple was demolished in 1879 by the Turk Pasha Chasekis to build the defensive wall of Athens. About 430 B.C. Height 0.45-0.47 m.

1780. (*Above*) Fragment of a plaque of the same frieze. Two wine skins and the calf of a figure. Height 0.23 m.

3646. Head of a statue of a young athlete or of Apollo. Found at Vouliagmeni, inside the shrine of Apollo Zoster in 1926. Delicate Attic work, post - Parthenonian, about 420 B.C. Height 0.23 m.

2756. Votive relief with simple, narrow epistyle. According to the inscription on the large poros base (in the room of the altar) it was the offering of Xenokrateia to Kephisos ; she is presenting the little Xeniades to a man. On the left Apollo is first, seated on a tripod, further to the right another seven gods. In the centre yet another man in front possibly the river Kephisos. At the edge the anthropomorphic body of the fore part of a bull, Acheloous. There are altogether 13 persons, including the Caryatid at the right edge, in the second plane (a frontal pose, with polos.). One of the best votive Attic reliefs of the period with artistic composition of the figures. About 410 B.C. Found outside New Phaleron, together with the adjacent no. 1783. Height 0.57 m., width 1.05 m.

1419. Fragment of a relief decree with a simple horizontal cornice. Four figures of men wearing the himation facing left and remains of an inscription: (name) *carved* [it]. Fine Attic work with an echo of the Parthenon. About 430 B.C. Unknown provenance. Height 0.50 m., width 0.34 m. (P l. 29 b).

254. Statue of a young athlete. Bending his head forward he lifts toward it his right hand in which he holds a metal crown to place on his head. Vivid contrast between the raised right shoulder and the lowered left. The left leg was stationary. A tender Attic work of the beginning of the 4th century B. C. based on an older Polykleitan original, Argive. Found at Eleusis (1887). Height 1.03 m.

176. Statue of Kore (Persephone) with its plinth. She wears an Ionian chiton and himation. She carried short torches in her hands (which were inserted). Fine Attic work about 420 B.C. with dependence on the works of Agorakritos. Found in Piraeus, it would have been an offering to the famous Thesmophorion. Height without the plinth 0.77 m. (Pl. 26)

1578. Torso of a statue of a woman. She is represented wearing a diaphanous peplos and she lifts the edges of her himation which covers her back and her body. Found in the village of Chonika in the Argolid. It would probably have come from the Argive Heraion. Acroterion ? A robust work, Doric, by an Argive artist, about 420 B.C., with Attic influence. Height 0.40 m.

226. Large votive relief. A woman in Argive peplos, standing facing right holds in her hand a divining liver. In front of her feet the lower trunk of a palm tree. She is probably the famous soothsayer Diotima of the Platonic Symposium. Found in her native town of Mantineia in 1887. An imposing work of an Argive sculptor about 410 B.C. showing influence of the technique of the Athenian sculptor Alkamenes. Height 1.48 m., width 0.80 m. (Pl. 30).

FROM THE ARGIVE HERAION

1571. Head of Hera, from a cult statue. Her hair, bound round by a flat band, falls behind to her neck. Found at the Argive Heraion. Work of an Argive artist of the school of Polykleitos, with Pheidian influence. The elaboration of the marble, somewhat hard, is reminiscent of the bronze tradition of the Argive workshops. The expression of the face has a serious, taciturn godliness. About 420 B.C. Height. 0.27 m. (Pl. 28 a).

3869. Torso of a female statue, wearing a sleeved chiton and himation. A bare arm passes obliquely behind the back. It is the hand of Cassandra who grasps the Palladium to save it from the attack of Ajax. Found at the Argive Heraion. It comes from the pediment (probably

the west) of the temple. Good work, early archaistic about
420 B.C. Height. 0.32 m.

1572. Torso of a warrior who rises to attack. Under
the right armpit a hand (probably a woman's) attached
in supplication. Height 0.50 m.

1573. Body of a warrior frontal with the head facing
right. In the centre of the panel the inside of a large shield,
once coloured. Height 0.76 m.

1574. Torso of an Amazon, frontal, the leg toward
the left, dressed in a peplos, the right breast bared. Height
0.49 m.

3500. Metope, relatively the best preserved. Movement of the figures toward the right. The left arm of a warrior who is engaged in a struggle with an Amazon. The
latter wears a sleeved short chiton and flees to the right.
On the left edge the chlamys of the warrior, wind-blown.
Height 1.06 m., depth 0.083 m.

1563. Head of a warrior with helmet.

1564. Head of an Amazon, the neck with a turn toward
the left. She wears the pointed Phrygian cap.

1561-1562 and **1567-69.** Heads of young men and women from the carved decoration of the temple. No 1562
with open mouth. The carving somewhat heavy but not
lifeless. The hair is rendered summarily.

1581-82. Fragments from the sima of the temple (Argive Heraion) with lion heads as water spouts which interrupt the relief decoration of leaves. Palmettes and lotus
flowers sprout from the spirals. Above the smaller of these
stand antithetic cuckoos, the birds of Hera. Height with
restoration 0.27 m.

3973. Fragment of the sima, with the best preservation
of the surface. Flowers and cuckoos. Length 0.46 m. (P l. 28 b)

1329. Votive relief with simple cornice, dedicated from Archandros to the Nymphs and Pan. On the left the dedicator « worships » in front of a simple open air altar. Higher, within the opening of a cave appears the upper body of Pan. Of the three Nymphs the two on the left are represented facing, the central one with a perpendicular direction of folds ; the right hand Nymph, from the side (only a little is preserved of her body). The inscription is on the front of the cornice. Found on the south slopes of the Acropolis in 1876. Exceptional Attic work of about 410 B.C. with studied composition and alternation of attitudes. Height 0.66 m., length 0.685 m.

3572. Part of a large votive relief. The cornice would have been horizontal. On the right below in relief Kore (Persephone) is seated, dressed in a diaphanous peplos. Standing behind her is Demeter, dressed in a peplos and with a himation which also covers her head. On the door-post, beside Demeter's left arm, is distinguished the beginning of her name, inscribed. With unusual plastic vitality the robust body of Demeter projects from the surface. Excellent Attic work of an important sculptor about 420 B.C. Found in 1925 in Athens (in the Byron settlement). It would have been an offering to the sanctuary of the Eleusinian divinities above the Ilissos (in Agrai). Height 1.15 m., width 0.53 m.

4531. Right part of a simple votive relief (choregic). On the right two masks, the one below comic, the upper one bearded (royalty or prophet). On the left, parts of two other tragic masks, the upper one bearded, in a lower plane. On the epistyle the remains of an engraved dedicatory inscription (of the donor) ... *os echoregi*. Excellent carving of the end of the 5th century B.C. with hieratic austerity. Found at Dionysos in Attica in 1955. Height 0.45 m., maximum width 0.295 m.

558. Head of Athena or some warrior, with Attic helmet. Surface much worn. Holes above the forehead for the insertion of parts of the helmet. The expression severe, the oblong face delicate. Good (island ?) work. About 430 B.C. Unknown provenance. Height 0.22 m.

4762. Statue of Kore (Persephone) headless, with its low plinth. She wears a chiton and himation, right leg at ease. The head with an inclination toward the left shoulder, the left arm bent. The lower body narrow with a perpendicular direction of the pleats on the left side. Good work of about 400 B.C., a replica of a somewhat older classical original. Found near the Olympeion in Athens. It would have been a dedication to the sanctuary of the Eleusinian divinities in the neighbouring suburb of Agrai. Height 1.20-1.22 m.

3854. Section of a base from a votive monument. On the front small figures in a low relief. A young man, nude, facing right, holds by the feet on his shoulders a nude standing youth with a shield. Behind, the upper body of another with Attic helmet and crest. According to the inscription it was the offering of youths (in the Pyrrhic dance) at the beginning of the Great Panathenaia. The remains of another inscription on the narrow right side refers to a victory in the great Dionysia. The back surface badly deteriorated in the background. End of the 5th or beginning of the 4th century B.C. Found in Athens in 1938. Height 0.33 m., maximum width 0.67 m.

3043. Statue of Aura (?) with its plinth. It has life-like movement toward the left, with the left leg bent. She wears a peplos (the left leg bared) and with the left hand she lifts high the edge of a cloak ; a low square hole at the back for strengthening. Fine Attic work about 410 B.C. probably the acroterion of some temple. From Athens. Height 0.67 m.

3569. Small head from a statue of Aphrodite (of the same type as the statue No. 1811, near the window). Contemporary replica of smaller size of a famous bronze original. Pleasant Attic work about 420 B.C. Found in Athens in 1924. Height 0.16 m.

3265. Statue of a goddess seated on a throne (Demeter ?) The head and arms are missing. She wears a chiton with a short overfold and a himation on the lower body and stands on a footstool. Copy of Roman times of some Pheidian original about 430 B.C. Found in 1912 in Athens (corner of Aeolus and Sophocles streets). Total height 1.12 m., depth of the throne 0.37 m.

1811. Statue of Aphrodite with round plinth. She lifts up her himation with her left hand, in the other she holds an apple. The himation creates a separate plane behind her body. A fine , accurate copy (of small size) of the first century A. D. of a famous original, probably bronze, formerly known from the copy in the Louvre as « Aphrodite Frejus » (today « Aphrodite Louvre-Naples »). Found at Epidauros in 1887. Height 0.60 m. The arms restored.

3949. Large statue of a goddess, with its plinth. She wears a chiton with rich folds and a himation, of which the weight falls above the stationery leg. The left arm inserted from the shoulder, in the hand she would have held a sceptre. Copy of the second century A. D. of a famous creation of some sculptor of the Pheidian period. About 430 B.C. There are several copies in other Museums. Found in 1934 in Athens (Praxiteles Street). Height with the plinth 1.90 m.

3279. Statue of Athena, headless, with plinth, rounded on one side and at the back. She wears a chiton and a long himation, the aegis with gorgon's head and rests her left hand on her hip. The prolongation of the plinth on the left shows that it would have carried a second statue. A diligent, lifeless copy of the second century A.D. of a classical original of about 400 B.C. Found in Attica. Total height 0.59 m., height of the plinth 0.075 m., length 0.37 - 0.38 m.

1776. Head of a goddess of over life size, with taciturn expression. Brought in 1890 from Kavokrio in Asia Minor (opposite Kalymnos). The torso remained there. Beginning of the 4th century B.C. Height 0.35 m.

3856. Head of a goddess, covered at the back with the himation. On each side of her long neck perpendicular folds. The face round with closed expression. A work somewhat crude but serious, of the beginning of the 4th century B.C. It belonged to a statue of a goddess rather than to a grave naiskos. Found in Athens in 1938. Height 0.33 m.

1501. Votive relief with horizontal cornice, known formerly by the name « The death of Socrates ». It is of the type of the funeral feast : a man extended on a couch holds the phiale of the libation. Around him are three other figures. A dog under the table. Good work with faultless preservation. Beginning of the 4th century B.C. Found in Piraeus. Height 0.51 m., width 0.63 m.

1389. Relief in the form of a simple shrine. In the centre Apollo seated on a tripod, with his chest bare, steps on the top step of a double base. On the right Leda wearing a peplos, on the left Artemis, leaning on her bow (?) with her lowered right hand. On the epistyle is preserved only the patronymic of the donor : ...*son of Bakchios erected* (this). About 410 B.C. one of the best contemporary works with Parthenon influence. Found in a house in Athens (Plaka) about 1840. It would probably have been an offering to the Pythion near the Olympeion. Height 0.70 m., width 0.69 m.

228. The upper torso of a large female statue (Aura or Nymph), with impetuous movement. The girded peplos is arranged in a rich curve, billowing and falling to the right obliquely, baring the right breast. With the raised left hand she lifts the edge of the himation. For the whole movement compare the small figure in the neighbouring room, no. 3043. The carving powerful, the plastic elevation as well as the rendering of the folds rich, grooved above the full body, suggest the post-Parthenon period. Found in 1890 to the east of the Stadion. It would have been perhaps the acroterion of one of the larger temples near the Ilissos. Height 0.60 m.

223. Small statue of Apollo. Nude, with lowered arms, he turns his head to the right. The greater part of the legs is missing. Copy of the second century B.C. of some important bronze original, probably Argive, about 440 B.C. Found in Sparta. Height 0.305 m.

4486. Torso of a small statue of Athena. She wears the girded Attic peplos, with aegis and himation. Modest copy of a famous original (work of Kresilas ?). One of the best copies is the « Athena Velletri » in the Louvre. Delicate work of the end of the 5th century B.C. Provenance unknown. Height 0.30 m.

1612. Torso of a statue of a nude Apollo. The type is known as the « Kassel Apollo ». Locks of hair on the shoulders. Copy of the Roman period of a famous original ; probably it would have been the « Apollo Parnopios », an early work of Pheidias. Found in Athens. Height 0.86 - 0.88 m. Compare the head no. 47, near the window.

47. Head of Apollo of over life size. Plaits at the back part of the head, locks on the temples, around the neck and throat. Excellent copy of the advanced first century A.D. of a famous original (compare no. 1612, nearby). Found in Athens in 1875, east of the Olympeion. Height 0.30 m.

158. Small statue of a goddess seated on a rock ; headless. She wears a girded chiton ; she lifts her himation above the left shoulder. A good small work and according to one opinion inspired by a figure of the west pediment of the Parthenon. Found at Epidaurus about 1838. Height 0.36 m., depth of the rock 0.28 m.

274. Small statue of Athena with elliptical base. She runs to the right holding her shield in her left hand. (On the back of it in relief a winged gorgon as an « emblem »). She wears a girded peplos, with many folds, windblown. Above the helmet a Sphinx, with the figure of Pegasos. A laboured work possibly reminiscent of the Athena of the east pediment of the Parthenon. According to the inscription on the base it was dedicated in 304 A.D. to Athena Hygeia. Found at Epidaurus in 1886. Height 0.70 m., height the of base 0.095 m.

275. Small statue of Athena with elliptical base. She runs to the left holding her shield in her left hand. She wears a chiton and peplos, on her chest the aegis with the gorgon's head. Inscription : « *At the order of the god, Alexander dedicated the goddess Athena to Artemis* ». Found at Epidaurus in 1886. About 300 A.D. Compare the adjacent no. 274. Height 0.63 m., height of the base 0.07 m.

3718. The « Athena of the Pnyx ». A large head of Athena, once inserted in a colossal statue, copy of a Pheidian original. Its type is that known as the « Medici Athena ». Compare the adjacent headless statues nos. 3000 and 1622. A cold work of the Antonine period (2nd century A. D.), the polishing of the marble imitating ivory. Found near

the Pnyx (west slopes of the Acropolis) in 1931. Height
0.70 m.

3000. Small statue of Athena, with its plinth, headless.
Her right leg slightly relaxed. Of the type of the « Athena
Medici » ; the original would have been a youthful work of
Pheidias. Product of the first half of the 2nd century A.D.
Found in Amalias (Elis). In the National Museum since
1911. Height 0.73 m. Compare the adjacent 1622.

705. Statue of Amazon - Caryatid, a relief standing on
a square base. On the front of the latter is the relief of a
shield (πέλτη), emblem of the Amazons. She is portrayed full
face, standing, with short chiton girded (half of the chest
bare), with the left leg at ease. On her head is a capital of
Corinthian type. The whole figure is recognized as inspired by the Amazon of Pheidias. It was found before
1830 in the Monastery of Loukou in Kynouria (Thyreatis),
where Herodes Atticus had a villa. This would have been
on the propylon of one of his buildings. Good work of the
2nd century A.D. Height 2.79 m.

1622. Small statue of Athena, headless. She wears a
chiton and girded peplos, and a short cloak falls from her
left shoulder. Laboured work of the first century A.D.
For its type see no. 3000. Found on Delos. Height 1 m.

3739. Part of the head of a female statue or relief. The
workmanship of the eye and the ear prove it to be a good
Attic product of about 420 B.C. Found in 1869 at the excavation of Panathenaic Stadium and compared with the
statue of « Aphrodite in the Gardens ». Height 0.17 m.

2182 - 2183. Two joined fragments from a relief plaque.
A dancer on her toes steps toward the left, with short diaphanous peplos. Provenance unknown. Height 0.57 m., width
0.12 m.

2184 - 2185. Fragments of two similar plaques. On one in mid air are the two legs of a dancer, on the other the two legs of another who dances on her toes. 1st A.D. copies of an enchantig original of the end of the 5th B.C. : these figures are from the «Laconian dancers» by the sculptor Kallimachos. The provenance and purpose of the plaques are not known. Height 0.26 m., width 0.14 m ; height 0.25 m., width 0.125 m.

200 - 202. Small statues, headless, copies at a smaller scale of figures of the west pediment of the Parthenon. No. 200. Kekrops with his daughter, height 0.41 m. Nos. 201-202. Two women seated on a rock. Height 0.33 m. and 0.41 m. Found at Eleusis in 1887 and 1888; they belonged, probably, to the pediment of a small shrine. Laboured workmanship of the 2nd century A.D.

3415. Part of a plaque with remains of a delicate low relief. A woman with girded peplos kneels on one knee, facing left. The chest frontal, the folds windblown to the right. It belongs to the frieze of Phigaleia. The fragment of the plaque with the head of the figure is in the British Museum. Found at Phigaleia in 1906 in the temple of Apollo. Height 0.41 m., width 0.35 m.

128. The « Lenormant Athena ». An unfinished statue, a modest copy of the Pheidian Athena of the Parthenon. On the shield are relief figures : the battle of the Athenians and Amazons. At the top of the high base (traces of figures) the birth of Pandora was represented. Found in 1859 in Athens, near the Pnyx. A work probably of the first century. A.D. Recognized by Lenormant as a copy of the Pheidian work. Total height 0.42 m., height of the base 0.07 m., width of the base 0.21 m.

177. Face of an acrolithic statue of a goddess, copy, probably, of a Pheidian gold and ivory statue. The eyes of ivory inserted, the pupils would have been of black stone, the eyelashes metal (traces are preserved). The surface of the marble polished. Grey from burning and from the disappearance of the colours. The locks of hair which are preserved on the left of the forehead are purple. Of the 2nd century A.D. Found in Athens, in the theatre of Herodes in 1857. Height 0.25 m.

1633. Small statue of the Parthenon Athena, headless. Probably of the beginning of the 4th century B.C., as is confirmed by the excellent carving and the rhythmically accented freedom of the leg. Unknown provenance. Height 0.80m.

129. The « Varvakeion Athena ». Statue of the Parthenon Athena, with its square base. It is the only one which gives (at 1/12 the original size) a simple, truthful idea of the chryselephantine Athena of the Parthenon by Pheidias (which was placed within the Parthenon in 447 B. C.). The goddess wears the Attic peplos. The overlap is girded with a snake. On the aegis on her breast are reliefs of coiling serpents, in the centre a gorgon. Two Pegasoi occupy the crest of the Attic helmet at the edges, at the centre a Sphinx. Perpendicular folds cover the right, the stationary leg. The small winged Victory would have held a fillet. It is placed standing on the right hand of Athena which rests on a column of a graceless and indeterminate type. With the other hand, lowered, she holds lightly the rim of the shield. A large serpent, Erichthonios, coils around the inside of the shield. On the outside a gorgon, with round face, winged. The back of the statue is not well finished. The bare parts of the original were of ivory, the garments of gold. Cold polishing on the face and the arms of our statue. It is not known whether the helmet was of bronze (as has been the theory). For the reliefs of the base of the original compare the adjacent Athena, no. 128. The rhythm of the balanced pose, square, without a turning of the head, expresses the godlike conception of the middle period of Pheidias. Though it is simplified in details, this statue apparently retained faithfully the analogies of the original. The Varvakeion copy is usually dated to the 2nd century A.D., recently, however, with persuasive arguments to the 3rd A.D. It is a valuable work as an archaeological proof ; as a work of art, uninspired, cold, and not pleasing. Found in 1880 near and north of the old Varvakeion. Total height with the base 1.105 m., height of the statue 0.94 m., height of the base 0.10 - 0.11 m., maximum width 0.405 m. (Pl. 31).

4491. The front part of the head of a goddess, of over life size, from a cult statue. Large eyes, locks of hair in waves above the temples. The prototype probably about 420 B.C. An imposing work, with lifelike spirit, from the workshop of Agorakritos. Unknown provenance. Height 0.38 m., maximum width (back) 0.36 m.

4527. Small statue of a goddess, headless, with chiton and himation. A poor work of the 2nd century A.D. Copy of an Aphrodite of Agorakritos, pupil of Pheidias, known as the « Aphrodite Doria » (from the better copy in Rome). Found in Athens. Height 0.68 m.

THE GARDEN

One of the two internal courts of the Museum which were provided by the architect Ziller was, before its post-war reconstruction, disorderly, shapeless, loaded with every kind of material. Wooden storecases with shelves, heavy with dusty, ancient marbles (the greater part of which were reliefs), were found on its southern side. An improvised shed in the centre was the carpenter's workroom. Some of the larger sculptures, for which there was no room in the show rooms, had been placed there, while a mass of « useless » sculptures had been piled up in the open air.

One thing, however, which offered spiritual comfort in the court itself was a fountain and also the six fig trees which a kindly guard had planted. The members of the Museum staff during the summers of the war were refreshed with their cool figs.

When all the ancient marbles had been methodically transferred to the new basement storerooms, or as many as seemed important to show rooms of the Museum, the area was transformed into a colonnaded court, with a simple cemetery and a garden in the centre. Grave stelai, several of small children, of the 4th century, as well as of the Hellenistic period, sepulchral lions, sarcophagi of the 2nd century A.D. were sheltered in the stoas. Only certain pieces which were found on the ocean bed off Antikythera in 1900 are without sepulchral purpose. These remnants, eaten by the salt, are worthy of attention because they are copies of important originals ordered by the Romans from neo - Attic workshops. The mosaic of Medusa which decorates the open air part of the garden was found in Piraeus.

The visitor, wearied by an extended tour of the Museum, accepts with relief this interval which stimulates thought and offers the charm of the open air.

To the left of the door :

882. Grave stele with simple pediment. A woman seated, facing left ; at her feet a dog. Simple work of the beginning of the 4th century B.C., with the overwhelming silence of loneliness. Found in Piraeus. It was in the archaeological collection there until 1888. Height 0.62 m., width 0.48 m.

Below the stairway:

Statues dragged up from the ocean bed off Antikythera in 1900 : Two horses from a chariot, two large statues of heroes of the Trojan cycle with lively movement. They are Odysseus and Diomedes engaged in the theft of the Palladion from Troy, a copy of some well-known bronze original of the classic period, the work probably of an Argive bronzeworker.

In the best state of preservation is the statue of a young satyr (who invites a Maenad to dance). The subject, of Hellenistic inspiration, is known from other copies of the Roman period.

The wreck of the ship which was carrying a cargo of sculptures to Rome is dated to the beginning of the first century B.C.

732. Grave stele of Kallisto, heavy, with pediment. The deceased, seated on a bench facing right, looking downward, lifts her himation in her left hand. On the right her servant girl holds a pyxis in front of her breast. The representation of the bending and the high girding of the barbaric chiton date the stele to the end of the 4th century B.C. In the central acroterion a low relief of a Siren. At the sides, a dove and an alabastron. On the epistyle the name : *Kallisto Philokratous Konthilethen*. Found in Attica in 1883. Height 1.70 m., width below 0.95 m.

3793. Grave stele in the form of a shrine with pediment in very low relief. On the left a bearded man, standing, with short chiton and chlamys, offers his right hand to a woman who stands facing him. The man holds in his left hand the reins of a horse whose head is drawn in deep relief between the two figures. On the cornice the remains of the inscription : *Aion, Nikomede*. About 340 B.C. Found in 1937 in Athens near the Sacred Way. Height 1.70 m.

3586. Grave stele of a young athlete in the form of a small shrine with pediment. He leans with his elbow on a column of the palaistra holding a strigil in his left hand. On the right facing him, a small servant, nude, holds, thrown over his shoulder, the himation of his master; in his left hand, an aryballos. His face has somewhat individual characteristics. On the epistyle is carved the name of the deceased : *Theomnestos Theophrastou Alaieus*. Middle of the 4th century A.D. Found at Laurion in 1925. Height 1.28 m.

1641. Large female statue, headless. She wears a peplos and himation with only the right part of her breast uncovered. The lower body narrow, the right leg relaxed. She wears a triple necklace, in relief. Worked also at the back except for a flat surface in the centre of the hairdress. Found with the following no. 1642, it is an eclectic work of the same period, probably from the same building. Height 1.85 m.

1642. Large female statue, headless. She stands firmly on the soles of her two feet, the right leg slightly bent. She wears a peplos with a long ungirded overfold; large round clasps on the shoulder. She wears four necklaces. The larger part of the back surface flat, unworked. The statue would have served as a Caryatid in the propylon of some building. A laboured, eclectic work of about 100 A. D. or later. Found in 1882 in Athens (Metropolis Square) together with no. 1641. Height 1.76 - 1.77 m.

3156. Sun clock in the form of a low chair with two animal feet. In front, over a hollow surface, twelve engraved lines; at the top a hole for the fixing of the metal hand. Found in the theatre of Dionysos. Height 0.50 m., width 0.40 m.

3661. Small grave stele of a boy with epistyle and roof tiles. He is dressed in a himation and plays with his dog, offering it a bird. On the epistyle the name : *Theokles*. Charm-

ing Attic work of the first half of the 4th century B. C.
Found in Attica. Height 0.59 m., width below 0.31 m.

4487. Grave stele in the form of a small shrine with
cornice. In the central acroterion, relief of a Siren as mourning singer. A young athlete, nude (3/4 body, facing left)
holds a bird in his right hand. Opposite, a small slave, nude,
with the athlete's strigil in his hand, raises his head toward
his master. The name of the latter is carved on the epistyle : *Aristion*. About 360 B.C. Found in 1940 in the Kerameikos. Height 1.38 m.

892. Small grave stele with pediment. A young girl is
represented looking down, with chiton and cloak, holding
a bird in her left hand. The red colour is preserved on her
hair and on her slippers. On the epistyle the inscription :
Choregis Choregionos. Second half of the 4th century B.C.
Found in Athens in 1882. Height 0.93 m., width below
0.44 m.

727. Grave stele, simple with low pediment. On the
right, seated on a stool, facing left, a bearded man receives
a young man, standing in front of him, clothed in a short
himation. On the epistyle the names : *Theodoros Oathen*,
Praxiteles Oathen. Found in Attica. End of the 5th century B.C. Height 1.02 m., width below 0.66 m.

763. Grave stele of a young girl, with pediment. She
is standing, facing left. Opposite, her mother caresses the
chin of the girl. On the epistyle the name of the deceased :
Mynnion Chairestratou Agnousiou. Second half of the 4th
century B. C. A laboured work but with human warmth.
Found in Athens (Stadiun Street) in 1888. Height 0.75 m.

3844. Sepulchral lion facing left. The front legs vertical
and the face turned slightly forward. The hind legs are
missing. Found probably in Attica. Length 1.42 m., height
0.58 m.

—. Large statue of Herakles, from the ocean bed off Antikythera, headless. It is a copy of a famous work of Lysippus, known from the better copy as the « Farnese Herakles ». The success of the Sicyonian artist lies in the combination of the pose with an emphasis on depth ; its relaxation is expressed with unprecedented ponderousness.

1184. Sarcophagus with simple cover. The relief representation is fairly low, and on only one side. In the centre, a plane tree in full leaf. On the left a centaur raises his club against a lion, on the right a similar figure against a panther. Below two smaller animals. Beginning of the 3rd century A.D. Found in Athens.

1312. Small grave stele of Philoxenos the Athenian, with pediment. He is portrayed seated on a stool, in reflective concentration in the manner of a philosopher. Facing him, motionless, his small slave. 2nd century B. C. Found on Rheneia. Height 0.83 m.

2779. A portrait statue of a Roman (?). He is represented as Dionysos holding a kantharos and a bunch of grapes. At his side, a small panther. A crude ugly work of the first half of the 3rd century A.D. Found in 1909 in Laconia, near Gytheion. Height with plinth 1.75 m.

1987. Fragment of a grave stele with cornice. Above the relief, doves at the edges, in the centre the lower body of a Siren (?). There is preserved the upper body of a young girl facing left, with mournful expression. On the epistyle is her name : *Strybele*. Found on the Sacred Way to Eleusis in 1903. Middle of the 4th century B.C. Height 0.36 m.

983. Small grave stele of a child holding a bird. Above the triangular finial a relief of a mourning Siren, in the corner a female mourner on her knees. Second half of the 4th century B.C. Found in Thebes in 1889. Height 0.72 m.

1245. Small grave stele of Lykios, with epistyle, doorposts and pediment. He is seated nude on a rock ; facing him, a small nude slave. Middle of the 2nd century B.C. Found on Rheneia. Height 1.07 m.

1313. Small grave stele of a Roman, shipwrecked. End of the Hellenistic period. Found on Rheneia. Total height 0.73 m.

1314. Small grave stele of Diodora with pediment. A bow above the figures. Height 0.70 m.

1315. Similar grave stele of Lysimachos and Lysimache. Beginning of the first century B.C. Found on Rheneia. Height 0.70 m.

1263. Similar stele of Philoumene. She is seated on a stool, covered up to her head with a himation of many folds. Provenance unknown. End of the 2nd century B.C. Height 0.85 m.

3534. Small statue of goat - footed Pan. The Arcadian god is represented wrapped in a himation, with his pipe in his left hand. Work of the Roman period, in accordance with a type of philosopher or orator of the 4th century B.C. Found in 1892 on the west slopes of the Acropolis (like no. 252 in the room of the altar). The legs restored below. Height of the ancient part 0.61 m.

4008. Attic sarcophagus, with heavy cover. In the principal scene Dionysos, a Satyr and Cupids symbolize the eternal « intoxication » of the Upper World. In the centre of the back a Cupid raises a heavy branch. Bucrania support the edges ; in vacant spaces, two lion heads. The rendering of the branch is impressionistic, with free use of the drill. On the narrow sides : A. Sphinx, B. Censer and two Cupids. End of the 2nd century A.D. Found in 1951 in Athens (Byron settlement). Height with cover (on the sides) 1.60 m., length 2.47 m.

243. Statue of Hermes carrying a ram. He wears a chlamys, and on his head the petasos, and carries in his left hand the herald's staff, in his other the horn of a goat which is at his side standing on its back legs. Crude graceless work of the 2nd century A.D. Copy of some good classical original of the 4th century B.C. Found at Troezen in 1890. Height with the restored edges of the feet 1.80 m.

When this room, the second of the classical grave stelai from 420 B.C. on, is reached, it becomes evident that the grave stele has taken on width and size, that the plan of the small shrine with doorway and pediment still predominates toward the end of the 5th century B.C. Inside the holy shrine are arranged two figures, facing one another, the first seated habitually facing toward the left, although there was no strict canon. The bodies touch the doorposts or appear in some strange way outside them. The feeling for space has not yet become compelling. There is progress, however, in the rendering of relief. The plasticity of the bodies takes on a new special rhythm from the beginning of the century.

Instead of the older spiritual simplicity there now dominates in the faces, in the poses, grief for the lost light of the sun ; the heads are bowed ; there appears a shocked sense of isolation. The expression of pathos is without rhetorical effect ; Attic nobility is diffused in the themes as in the faces and the hands. Apart from the stelai, marble lekythoi, which at times take on unaccustomed size, raise in the cemeteries of Attica their slender bodies which become evermore graceful.

3624. Grave stele of Hegeso, daughter of Proxenos. It has the form of a shrine with pediment and with floral acroteria. Hegeso, seated on a carved chair, facing left, dressed in chiton and himation, with diaphanous veil over her bowed head, holds an open pyxis with jewels which her servant, facing her, proffers. The servant wears the barbaric sleeved chiton and ungirded peplos, her head wrapped in a net, slippers on her feet. Hegeso rests her feet on a low footstool, her hair at the back gathered into a snood. A silent grief suffuses the faces of the two women. Over the azure colour of the background would have gleamed the painted golden jewels, which Hegeso held in her right hand. Her name is inscribed on the epistyle. Found in the Kerameikos, with a later construction of the tomb. This, the noblest of the Attic grave steles, giving immortatity to the Athenian lady, is the work of

a leading scupltor, if not of Kallimachos himself, of some asso-
ciated artist, his pupil. Height of the central acroterion
1.58 m. (Pl. 32).

To the left of the door :

765. Grave stele of Mika and Dion in the form of a
small shrine with relief pediment. On the left the former,
seated on a stool, holds a mirror in her left hand, while with
her other she welcomes the standing Dion. The names carved
on the epistyle. Found in the Kerameikos in 1870. About
430 B.C. It has a classic harmonious serenity. Only the expression of the young man is sad. Height 0.90 m. width 0.49 m.

2584. Sepulchral marble lekythos, with relief decoration.
In the centre, a youth and a woman facing one another. On
the left a bearded man, on the right another woman. Above
his shoulder is inscribed : *Oros mnematos.* Found in Athens
in 1904. The neck and rim restored. Beginning of the 4th
century B.C. Height of the ancient part 1.10 m.

2894. Grave stele of unusual heaviness. On the upper
surface two holes (one with lead) for the clamp of the
upper part. Two men, face to face, the left a youth, the
right a bearded man with aryballos hung from his left arm.
In the centre, a dog. About 410 B.C. The tender relief suggests the hand of an Ionian artist. The form of the stele
is non-Attic. Found in 1910 near the Dipylon. Height 1.03 m.,
width 0.056 m., depth 0.225 m.

754. Roof of a grave monument from the Polyandrion cemetery in Athens. The relief decoration long and
simple, arching above, lower gradually toward the edges.
At the highest central point, a palmette of many petals,
with the central petals antithetic sprouts from acanthus
leaves, arising from spirals. On each side, a lotus flower,
rosettes and, at the edges, a half flower. On the epistyle the names of the Athenian horsemen who fell in the

battles of Corinth and Koroneia in 394 B.C. (Among others the name of Dexileus). Found in 1861 outside the Kerameikos. This is one of the choicer and better carved examples of decorated monuments. The plastic elevation of the petals corresponds to the grooving of the spirals below. The whole has a pure articulation, symmetry and a certain austerity. Length 2.25 m., maximum height 0.48-0.50 m.

2744. Relief plaque, part of a grave monument. It was placed by the city of Athens in the street leading to the Academy (Polyandrion), to honour the horsemen and hoplites who fell at Corinth and Koroneia in 394 B.C. Above the stele, traces of the carved names. Higher up the relief : a horseman at the gallop and a standing hoplite. In the middle on the ground a fallen hoplite nude, with a skilfully executed turning of the body. Found northeast of the Dipylon in 1907. About 390 B.C. Height 0.60 m., width 0.67 m.

922. Small grave stele in the form of a small shrine, with low pediment. On the left a woman seated on a stool facing right, dressed in Argive peplos, holds with her two hands the arm of a girl who stands facing her. A modest but tender work of the end of the 5th century B.C. Provenance unknown. Height 0.74 m.

902. Grave stele of Tynnias with pediment. He is portrayed quietly seated on a chair, facing right, holding a staff. The name inscribed on the pediment. Attic work of the beginning of the 4th century B.C. with Parthenon influence. It was in the Piraeus collection until 1888. Height 0.58 m.

2589. Small painted grave stele of Lysimachos and Polykrite, with simple frame. Formerly the drawing was discernible : on the left a figure with himation toward whom a child opposite raises his hands. Red colour in the carved letters, a red band on the upper frame. End of the 5th century B.C. Found in Attica. Height 0.42 m., length 0.28 m.

831. Large grave stele of Phrasikleia with pediment. On the left the deceased is seated on a stool, facing right, with head bowed. Behind her left leg appears the upper body of a young girl (the head missing). On the right standing, her servant in barbaric dress holds the pyxis with the jewels. Skilful rendering of the folds of the chiton and of the himation of Phrasikleia. The name is inscribed on the flat epistyle. Found in the Kerameikos in 1819. Height 1.75 m.

835. Large marble lekythos, with relief representation. A young man, mounted, facing right, behind two standing hoplites who join hands in « welcome ». The shield of the first, held high, isolates the two figures as if it were magic circle. At the back and between the two figures, two ethereal women in low relief. The first is seated on a stool facing left and leaning on her shoulder at the back is a girl with bowed head (her hair like a youths). Colour would have covered the nude part of the body. The scene itself, delicately chiselled, comes from some well-known artist's original, a work perhaps of the painter Parrhasios. The horse is extended at length on the rounded surface, with impressive simplicity in the hind part of its body. Red colour covered the lower body of the vase. About 420 B.C. Found in 1849 near the old Senate house (Boule). It would have been placed in the ancient cemetery outside the Themistoclean wall. The three young men, members of the same family, would have been killed in the Peloponnesian War. The two female figures welcome them to the Elysian Fields. The vase was fastened with lead to its ancient round base (where there is a later inscription). The upper neck is missing. Height of the vase (without the restoration) 1.58 m., height with the base 1.80 m.

3790. Large grave stele of a young mother. It has the form of a small shrine with pediment (the central acroterion high).

Seated on a stool facing left she gazes sorrowfully with bowed head toward her child who is held by a beautiful girl facing her. The child extends his left hand in an eager manner towards his mother. Excellent Attic work, harmonious and human, probably by the same artist who created the adjacent stele of the two women, no. 726. Beginning of the 4th century B.C. Found in Athens (Psychiko) in 1937. The lower part restored. Height of the ancient part 1.50 m.

726. Grave stele of a woman, with pediment. The deceased seated on a stool, with head bowed, gazing mournfully at the pyxis which the girl facing her is holding. The latter, standing, has one leg relaxed ; the outlining of the leg is rhythmically and plastically drawn. A work worthy of notice, it shows development, with dramatic isolation, of the theme of Hegeso. From the same artist is also the large adjacent stele no. 3790 and (later) the beautiful head, No. 2582. Beginning of the 4th century B.C., in the Piraeus collection until 1888. Height 1.26, width 0.77 m.

2582. Head of a girl (servant ?) from a grave stele, in deep relief. She is represented as slightly bent toward the seated deceased. Part of an important stele, it would be a later work of the same artist as the one who carved the adjacent no. 726. Found in 1904 in Athens. Height 0.28 m.

3780. Grave stele, with greyish colour caused by fire. The subject the same as that of the stele no. 726 ; the carving, however, is more mediocre. Fine throne with a Sphinx on its support, which terminates with the head of a ram. Beginning of the 4th century B.C. Found in the Mesogeia of Attica in 1936. Height 1.20 m., width 0.63 m.

In the case by the wall : Three white ground lekythoi from tombs at Eretria. Nos **V. 1955 - 56** are works of the «Women painter». Three - figured composition. Seated on the steps of

her pillar (stele) the deceased in no. 1955 mourns with
uplifted hands. Dull black for the outline, the polychrome
colouring of the garments is preserved. The soft violet colour of the left figure of no 1955 helps to show her nobility. 420-410 B.C.

723. Grave stele of Polyxene in the form of a small
shrine with acroterion. Seated, facing right, on a well-drawn
stool, the young woman dressed in chiton and himation,
which also covers her head, bends sorrowfully toward her
small boy who leans against her knees. Behind is a girl,
standing. Inscription on the epistyle. Attic work of a sensitive artist of about 400 B.C. Found in the Kerameikos.
Height 1.75 m., width below 1.85 m. (Pl. 33 a).

939. The upper part of a grave stele, with floral relief
decoration : in the centre a palmette above spirals and
an acanthus, framed on each side by a half palmette. On
the smooth surface of the stele the name of the deceased :
Nausikrates Sokratous Agnousios. Middle of the 4th century
B.C. Found in Piraeus in 1831. Height 0.76 m., width 0.30 m.

3069. Part of a large grave stele. The upper body of
a woman facing right ; her head covered by her himation
is bowed. 1st half of the 4th century B.C. Found in Athens
in 1896. Height 0.67 m.

3891. Part of a grave stele, narrow. The figure in relief, frontal. A girl is supported, by her left elbow, on
the disk of a loutrophoros in relief, with her left leg crossed. She wears chiton and himation, and lifts its edge with
her fingers. Head and feet are missing. Delicate work inspired by some important original. About 410 B.C. Found
in Athens or in Attica in 1942. Height of the ancient part
0.64 m.

3472. Grave stele of Ktesileos and Theano. It terminates in a pediment with floral acroteria. On the right seated on a stool, Theano, facing left, dressed in chiton and a himation the edge of which she lifts forward with her hand. Opposite, standing, her husband, Ktesileos, leans, with his left arm - pit on his staff, and with hands clasped watches Theano in sorrow. On the epistyle the names in the genitive. The background would have been coloured azure. Noble work of a good sculptor, with a somewhat affected attention to the rendering of the folds. Found in 1921 in Athens. Height 0.93 m., width 0.50 m.

717. Grave stele, three-figured. On the left, seated, facing right, on a polished stool, is a woman whose feet, in high sandals, rest on a footstool. Facing her is discernible a girl, standing. Looking toward the latter, with head bowed, stands a bearded man in himation, in the centre behind the seated woman. The figures in deep relief. It lacks its pediment which would have extended well beyond the columns, unusually narrow and high. Found in 1870 in the Kerameikos. It may have been placed by the parents on the tomb of their daughter, but the exceedingly mournful expression of the seated woman suggests the hypothesis that she is the deceased and that the father is looking toward his orphaned daughter. Fine work of a classical composition, with a certain grandeur, of the beginning of the 4th century B.C.

752. Grave stele of Demokleides, son of Demetrios. It is crowned above with cornice and with roof tiles. The small figure is confined to the upper right edge. Seated on the ground, facing left, a hoplite, with knees raised, in a short chiton, rests his head in sorrow on his right hand. Behind him on the ground the shield and spear, and in front of him the prow of a galley. All below would have been coloured blue to indicate the sea. The name is carved on the epistyle above the figure. The stele would have been placed on the cenotaph of a hoplite who lost his life in some naval battle. Unknown provenance. Height 0.67 m., width 0.45 m.

718. Grave stele of Ameinokleia, with pediment. The young woman standing, facing left, covered with a himation as far as her head, rests her hand on the head of a kneeling small servant who helps her put on sandals. On the left another young woman, standing, holds the pyxis with the jewels. This mediocre work is a copy of an unknown contemporary creation, with the original subject in larger dimensions and with beautiful composition (see the fragment of another copy no. 2042 by the wall). Beginning of the 5th century B.C. Found in Piraeus in 1836. Height 1.37 m., width about 0.71 m.

2042. Part of a grave stele. It was a contemporary copy of a famous original, known from the smaller adjacent stele no. 718. No. 2042 would have had the dimensions of the original. Found in Athens. Height 0.53 m., width 0.34 m.

1993. Part of a grave stele. A young servant raises in her hand a puppet (doll) toward the deceased, a small girl whose figure is not preserved. Beginning of the 4th century B.C. Found in Athens in 1873. Height 0.66 m.

724. Grave stele of Phainarete, with pediment and acroteria. The name on the epistyle. The young woman is seated on a stool, her head bowed in sorrow. Of the facing figure is preserved part of the head and part of the right arm. Beginning of the 4th century B.C., one of the fine works of the period. Found in Attica. Height 1.60 m., width 0.85 m.

2004. Grave stele with horizontal epistyle. Bearded man, nude, facing right, with the stance of a wrestler (for the pankration ?). Above the epistyle is carved his name :

Agakles Phryn(ichou). Probably about 420 B.C. Found in Attica in 1857. Height 1.13 m., width 0.65 m.

778. Small grave stele with horizontal cornice. The relief in a square hollow : a bearded man, seated on a chair, facing left, wrapped in a himation, holds in each of his hands a bird and offers them to two boys standing in front of him. Above on the bare plaque is carved his name : *Euempolos*. Modest but good, human work of the end of the 5th century B.C. Found in Piraeus. Height 0.54 m.

1822. Grave stele of a woman, with pediment. She is portrayed seated with breast « en face », holding a mourning band. On the left, facing her, another woman, standing, holds a pyxis. The perpendicular folds of her peplos, as well as the robust body of the seated woman, and also her heavy hands support the theory that it is the work of some Peloponnesian, possibly Argive sculptor who studied in Athens. About 420 B.C. Found in Athens in 1898, the upper part with the heads of the figures in 1964. Height 1.08 m., width 0.70 m.

1826. Statue of a young « Diadoumenos ». An athlete or god (Apollo ?) nude with a broad fillet around his hair. The head is turned to the right as is the bent leg. The spread arms give a certain broadness to the upper part of the body. Good copy of about 100 B. C. of a famous bronze original ; work of the Argive Polykleitos (about 430 B.C.). The original would have belonged to the later period of Polykleitos, with Attic influence. The prop beside the right leg is the addition of the copyist. The gesture of the arms is not yet well understood. Found on Delos in 1890. Height 1.95 m.

3153. Votive relief, square, simple. A young man, nude, standing, facing right, in front of a horse holds the reins and a spear. The figure is reminiscent of the famous Doryphoros of the Argive bronze worker Polykleitos. Probably of the beginning of the 4th century B.C. Found in Argos. Brought to the National Museum in 1900. Height 0.51 m., width 0.37 m.

3622. Sepulchral statue of a woman, with a round, smooth plinth. She wears a chiton ; the himation covers her head which is slightly bent downward. With her right hand she holds in front of her breast the edge of the himation, which is diagonally pleated from her shoulder to her lowered left hand. She steps forward on both feet with the left knee bent. All the weight of the folds is centred on her left side ; linear rendering of the hair. A work, somewhat rough, of the first century A.D.; copy of a noble creation of some important sculptor, about 320 B.C.. The head has portrait characteristics, somewhat idealized. The type is known as the « tall woman from Herculaneum ». Found in the old cemetery of Stadium Street, near Constitution Square in 1926. Height 2 m.

3283. Grave stele of Ameinodora, rectangular, with pediment. A girl is standing, full face, with a melancholy inclination of the head toward the right. The name carved on the epistyle. Fine, noble Attic work of the beginning of the 4th century B.C. Found in 1913 in the bed of the Ilissos. Height of the ancient part 1.32 m.

4519. Grave stele, carved on both sides, with simple termination above. On one side a loutrophoros, on the other a lekythos. The figures which were drawn on the sculptured pots are effaced. First half of the 4th century B.C. Found in 1955 outside of Athens. Total height 1.20 m.

3964. Grave stele of Pausimache, with pediment. The young girl standing, facing right, with slight bending in her pose, inclines her head toward the mirror which she holds in her left hand. On the epistyle a four line epigram. Tender work of the beginning of the 4th century B.C. with lyric feeling. From the same workshop as the related stele in this room no. 4006. Found in Attica in 1948. Total height 1.24 m., width below 0.44 m., above 0.41 m.

2578. Grave stele of Stephanos, rectangular, with pediment : many petalled palmette, with a Sphinx on each side. From the hollowed surface of the background emerges the figure in relief : a young athlete, nude, facing left (the body frontal) with a chlamys on the shoulder holds a strigil and an aryballos. On the left his dog. Above the narrow epistyle is carved his name : *Stephanos*. Found at Tanagra in 1904. Fine work of a local artist. Beginning of the 4th century B.C. Height 1.37 m.

884. Grave stele of Panaitios. The upper and the right parts, missing, made up with plaster. In slight relief in the centre is a loutrophoros, on the left a lekythos (on the right the corresponding one is missing). On the loutrophoros a warrior in relief standing in front of his horse *(Panai-*

tios Amaxanteos, according to the inscription) receives a bearded man. Behind him a small boy. On the lekythos a young boy, nude, runs holding a wheel, a children's plaything. Bands and an alabastron on the stele. First half of the 4th c. B.C. Found in the Dipylon about 1880. Height of the ancient part 1.52 m., length 0.82 m.

4006. Grave stele of a girl. On the rounded pediment, relief of a mourning Siren with spread wings. The girl standing facing right, holds a flower (?) in her left hand, bending her head in sorrow. In front of her, standing, a small servant. On the epistyle the remains of the name ... *ine Demokleos.* About 380 B. C. One of the finer works of this kind from this period. Found in 1952 outside of Athens. Height 1.51 - 1.52 m.

3614. Heavy plaque, probably from a frieze, with three figures in relief. In the centre a nude warrior with high Corinthian helmet, with the shield on his left arm and a hanging chlamys. Holding his sword in his right hand he rushes against an Amazon armed with a shield. On the right another Amazon, facing front, runs toward the left, fleeing from the pursuit of a warrior who would have been portrayed on the adjoining plaque. On the upper surface holes for the attachment of the metal clamps. About the middle of the 4th century B.C. Found in 1926 in Athens. It recalls in its subject as well as in its technique the friezes of the Mausoleum. It is possibly the work of one artist (Bryaxis ?) who worked there as well as in Athens. Height 0.55 m., width 1.08 m.

218. The « Hermes of Andros ». Statue, probably sepulchral, of Hermes as « the conductor of souls ». He is represented nude, with the chlamys on his left arm, and with his left leg relaxed. A serpent surrounds the heavy support. Found in 1833 at Palaiopolis on Andros. Copy probably

of the 1st century B.C. of an important Attic original, Praxitelean. The legs restored in plaster. Height 1.96 m.

2308. Epikranion of a high, rectangular grave stele.
Palmette with separated petals rises above the spirals which
sprout from a spreading acanthus. Beautiful hollowing of
the stems of the spirals . Of the same slab of marble, the
back of the rounded plaque is separated by a deep groove. One
of the best and most remarkable of its kind in its conception : the palmette contains in its form the symbolism of
resurrection after death. About the middle of the 4th century B.C. Found in Athens. Height 0.76 m.

720. Grave stele of Melite, wife of Spoudokrates of
Phlyous. It has the form of a shrine with pediment ; on
the epistyle the inscription. Melite is portrayed full face,
supported by her left elbow on a pillar while she raises
with her right hand the edge of her himation. The figure
preserves some of the divinity of the original which inspired it. Found in Piraeus in 1836. Middle of the 4th century B.C. Height 1.70 m., width below 0.81 m.

794. Grave stele of an ephebos. It lacks the upper and
the lower parts. The youth is portrayed full face. The rich
folds of the himation fall on the right, beside a pilaster
where a hare is standing. The chronology of this work
is debatable. The body has classical rhythm, but there
are other considerations such as its unaccustomed depth
which suggest a later period (late Hellenistic ?). Found
at Laurion. Height 0.63 m., width 0.51 m.

1827. Statue of the type of the « small woman of Herculaneum ». Fine work of the Hellenistic period with skilful rendering of the folds, which have plastic volume
and spirit. The original, an undoubtedly famous postpraxite-

lian work of about 300 B. C Copy of the 2nd century B.C.
Found on Delos in 1894. Compare the adjacent no 3622.
Height 1.80 m. (P l. 33 b).

ROOM OF THE ALTAR

In this area of the Museum, which joins the old building with the new wing, was formerly housed the Museum's rich collection of bronzes. The room was elliptical inside at the eastern end and in form well - matched with the remaining section. The back garden of the Museum with the tall pines and cypresses extended along this whole side of the street.

In the post-war arrangement there was an attempt to make use of this room, which has a somewhat amorphous shape, to give with its exhibits some idea of an ancient shrine. No grave monument would be given a place among the dedications to the gods of the shrines which the ancient people would have wished to be free of the shadow of death.

Around the central altar were placed the votive statues and reliefs from different shrines. Some are works of good sculptors, others simple, devout offerings to different gods, especially to Herakles, Aphrodite, the Nymphs, and to goat-footed Pan. From the shrine of Herakles in the area of Agrai on the Ilissos come the two reliefs on the left of the shrine (Nos. 1778, 2668). There is still preserved there, nearby, the cave of Pan where Socrates worshipped, beseeching the gods to grace him not with wealth but with the inner, the true beauty.

303. Statue with its round base. Around an unfluted column the three-figured Hekate, fearful goddess of the crossroads. Found at Epidauros in 1884. According to the inscription it was a dedication of Favulus to Artemis Hekate. A cold work of the late Roman period. Total height 0.76 m.

252. Statue of Pan. He is portrayed as serious, wearing a himation (of the type of statues of philosophers), holding the pastoral pipe. Copy of the first century A.D. of a graceful original of the 4th century B.C. From Sparta (1879). Height 0.89 m.

4465. Votive relief in the form of a shrine; offering to the three Nymphs who are portrayed at the left. The himation covers also their bowed heads. In front of Hermes, and smaller, is Pan who carries a hare hung above his shoulder from a sling. On the right three worshippers of small height. The relief is wedged into its circular unworked base, no. **4465a**. Excellent classical Attic work of about 460 B.C. Found inside the cave of Pentelikon with the somewhat later relief no. 4466. Height 0.53 m., width 0.75 m. (Pl. 36).

4466. Attic work in the form of a cave ; offering to the Nymphs. The figures in the background with strong relief projection. Of the three Nymphs on the left the first is seated. Further to the right Hermes standing and Pan seated with the pipe in his hand. On the simple square, unworked base is the carved inscription : *Agathemeros offered* (this) *to the Nymphs*. Found on Pentelikon in 1952 in the same cave as the other relief no. 4465. Last quarter of the 4th century B.C. Noteworthy is the representation of space in the middle of which stand the figures. Height 0.70 m., height of the base 1.04 m.

1966. Votive relief, simple. On the left, facing right, Apollo seated, a small Pan, Hermes, and three Nymphs, looking forward, in dance formation. On the right are lightly sketched six figures of worshippers. Found in 1900 on the south slopes of the Acropolis. A significant work of archaistic trend. Middle of the second century B.C. Length 0.73 m., height 0.38 m.

230. Marble statue of Apollo Kitharodos with its square poros unworked base. Apollo (the head and left arm are missing) wears the sleeved chiton of the musician and the himation. According to the inscription on the base it was an offering by Aristomenes the Thessalian and Nikon the Athenian to Apollo Aigileus. Found in 1889 on the island Aigileia by Kythera. 4th century B.C. Height of the statue 1 m., of the base 0.27 m.

1495. Large altar with three steps. According to the inscription on the face of one side it was dedicated by the Boule of the Athenians to Aphrodite Hegemone and the Graces. The upper surface, unworked, finishes at the sides with « cushions » and with elegant spirals. About 210 B.C. Found near the Theseion in 1891. Height 1.43 m., width 1.40 m. (with the step).

1390. Small votive relief. On the right seated comfortably on a throne a large figure of a woman who holds a phiale in her right hand. She is leaning with her elbow on a support upon which is carved the inscription : *Epiktesis.* Below, above a base, is a statue of a woman who holds a basket in her two hands. On the front face of the base is the name : *Euthenia.* On the edge at the back a tree with branches which a small woman has climbed. She raises her left hand in a « gesture » or in order to gather fruit. Upon the bare plaque of the relief and in front of the first woman is the name : *Telete.* The symbolic representation is difficult to interpret. The figure of Telete with its godlike grandeur recalls the Pheidian Aphrodite. It was found in 1820 in the monastery of Loukou in Kynouria, where Herodes Atticus had a villa. Work of the 2nd century A.D. Height 0.51 m., length 0.35 m.

683. Small statue of Pan seated on a round rock with his goat feet doubled underneath him, on the skin of an animal which covers his back as well. He would have held his pipe with his two hands. The movement is slightly antithetic. Work of the Hellenistic period. The type, known from other copies, recalls a lively older creation. Found in Athens (Olympeion) in 1861. Height 0.47 m.

1778. Attic relief, an offering to Zeus Meilichios. The god is portrayed seated on the left, behind him traces of the body of a goddess who holds a horn. Farther to the right

Hermes facing forward, on the edge Herakles (the lion skin covers his head). In front of the chair of Zeus a mask in relief of Achelous. Below is carved his name. Laboured work of the 3rd century B.C. Found in the Ilissos in 1893. Height 0.85 m., width 0.58 m.

253. Small statue of Herakles. It lacks the part below the knee. Supported on the left leg. The head is covered with the lion skin which is fastened in a knot on the chest. The deep set eyes give pathos to the square head. Fine work of the 2nd half of the 4th century B.C. The type recalls an important Attic original. Found in Athens in 1885. Height 0.54 m.

2668. Heavy plaque with five relief figures. On the right an athlete advances, behind him a woman, Athena, Nike, and a dadouchos. Probably the base of some offering or shrine. Found in the bed of the Ilissos in 1893. The surface badly deteriorated. Beginning of the 4th century B.C., probably. Width 1.65 m., height 0.92 m.

1404. Votive relief in the form of a shrine with simple cornice. On the left Herakles, nude, stands upright in front of a small building (three steps, a column, and horizontal cornice). On the right, lower, a pilgrim, wearing the himation, « worships » leading a cow and a lamb. Behind, traces of another figure. Beginning of the 4th century B.C. Found probably at Ithome. Height 0.49 m., length 0.52 m.

2723. Votive relief with simple horizontal cornice. In the centre above, with two steps, a building, simple, with four columns, the two behind with slight perspective. On the right Herakles, nude, full face, extends his hand to a standing youth. At the back on the left a man wearing the himation, the father of the youth, « worships ». Found at Marousi, built into the wall of the small church of Aghios

Dimitrios, in 1897. Middle of the 4th century B.C. Height 0.47 m., length 0.58 m.

1783, 2756. Two poros bases with inscriptions of the donors. Above them the plaster casts of the marble reliefs which are in the room of the votive statues of the classical period : 1783 (double relief). Offering of Kephisodotos, son of Demogenes ; 2756. Offering of Xenokrateia. End of the 5th century B. C. Found in Athens. (See the description in the pertinent room. Height of the base 1783 : 1.90 m., height of the base 2756 : 1.60 m. (without the plaster part of the modern base).

3617. Plaque, simple, square, with relief decoration : Herakles, frontal, nude, raises his club in his right hand, beating the Lernaean Hydra, while he steps with his left foot on the body of the serpent. The lion skin hangs from his left arm. On the ground to the left, the crab, the helper of the Hydra. Found in Argive Lerna (Myloi). Fairly good work of a local sculptor possibly of the 3rd century B.C. Height 0.67 m., width 0.58 m. (P l. 35).

227. Torso of a statue of Aphrodite. The lower body was cut from another piece of marble ; a bracelet around the left arm. Copy of a work of the ripe period of Praxiteles (the so-called Aphrodite of Arles, in the Louvre, is the best of the copies). Work of the late Hellenistic period, with careful attention to the carving of the marble. Found in Athens. Height 0.67 m., width 0.55 m. (P l. 34).

1451-52. Plaques of a frieze with reliefs of naked Erotes who flee to the left holding censers and oinochoes. Found on the north slopes of the Acropolis, where there was a shrine of Aphrodite and Eros. They would possibly have formed the boundary of the temenos. End of the 2nd century B.C. The plaque no. 1452, as well as the fragment (on the wall, no. 3969) laboured works of repair from the Roman pe-

riod. 1451 : Height 0.46 m., length 1.21 m., width 0.24 m.
1452 : Height 0.46 m., length 0.78 m., depth 0.22 m.

1591. (By the wall). Fragment of a heavy relief plaque.
Eros advances, nude, holding a censer. Found at Daphni,
in the shrine of Aphrodite in 1891. For the theme
and use see the adjacent plaques, nos. 1451 - 1452. A work
probably of the 4th century B.C. Height 0.28 m., width
0.26 m.

1601. Small relief, probably votive. The upper part
in the form of a cube was decorated with low relief in its
square compartment. On the right Aphrodite standing,
facing left, leaning against a tree, holds a phiale in her right
hand. Facing her a small suppliant, wearing a himation.
Traces of an inscription on the lower part. Found at Daphni.
For the type of Aphrodite see the adjacent torso no. 1604.
Total height 0.42 m., width above 0.31 m., below 023 m.

1592 - 93. Two marble doves, offerings to Aphrodite
of Daphni. Above the larger is carved the name of the donor : *Phalakron offers* (this) *to Aphrodite.* Found at Daphni in 1891-92. Length 0.20-0.25 m.

1600. Small statue of a girl, headless, with the plinth. She
wears a chiton girded high and a short chlamys, drawn diagonally below the breast and at the back. The arms are
missing, formerly inserted. Delicate, graceful Attic work of the
beginning of the 3rd century B.C. Found in 1891 at Daphni.
It had been placed in the shrine of Aphrodite. Height 0.46 m.

1604. Torso of a statue of Aphrodite, dressed in a light
chiton. She leaned against a tree with her left elbow; the
himation, folded, falls at her left shoulder. Found at Daphni.
The whole statue, a cult statue in the temple, would have
been a contemporary replica of a well - known work erected
in Athens, of the « Aphrodite in the Gardens » by the hand

of the sculptor Alkamenes. About 420 B.C. Height 0.35 m., length about 0.46 m.

1597. Votive relief. The upper part is missing with the heads of the figures. In the centre Aphrodite, full face. Eros touches her lightly with the palm of his left hand. On the right a figure wearing a peplos ; left, by the side of Aphrodite, an altar and a small suppliant. On the left edge the lower body of a woman full face. Excellent Attic work about 420-410 B.C. Found in 1892 at Daphni, in the shrine of Aphrodite. Height 0.43 m., width 0.57 m.

1449. Votive relief in the form of a cave. The three Hours (Hores) advance in dancing step toward the right with windblown himatia. Facing them Pan seated, with feet doubled under, on a rock, plays his pipe. The third Hora carries ears of wheat, the second has her head raised, the first gazes calmly forward. Though typical, the figures suggest in their theme a poetic symbolism. Second half of the 4th century. It is not certain whether the relief was found at Sparta or at Megalopolis. Height 0.55 m., width 0.73 m.

1455. Votive relief, heavy, from hard Boeotian stone. It represents in low relief the figure of Helikon, hairy, bearded, who rushes forth from the mountain. According to the engraved inscription it was dedicated to the Muses and to Helikon by Amphikritos. In the inscription is also mentioned the name of Hesiod. A crude, but expressive work of the Hellenistic period. Found at Thespiae, close to the shrine of the Muses in 1889. Height 1.19 m.

251. Statue of Pan, in deep relief. Together with the base it formed the support of a large open air table. For the type of Pan see the adjacent no. 252. Work of the 2nd century A.D. Found in Piraeus in 1839. Total height 1.12 m., of the statue 0.92 m.

1454. Votive relief. Herakles rests under the shade of

a plane tree. On the right are preserved the leaves in low relief. Work of the 2nd century A.D., copy of a fresh Hellenistic work. Found in Athens in 1887. Height 0.76 m., width 0.88 m.

3943. Heavy plaque, decorated with two wreaths of ivy and olive in relief. Below, a horizontal projection with cornice. Remains of the frieze of the small choregic monument which Thrasyllos erected at a high level below the southern rock of the Acropolis. Above it was placed a bronze tripod. Height 0.45 m., width 1.12 m.

257. Statue of Papposilenus, with himation on the lower body. On his left shoulder sits the little Dionysos who holds a tragic mask of Silenus above the right shoulder. Good work probably of the Hellenistic period, copy of an orginal of the 4th century B.C. The face of Silenus seems to be inspired by a portrait statue of Socrates. Found in the Theatre of Dionysos in 1832. Height 1.17 m.

1626. Torso of a male .statue (an athlete apoxyomenos). The left arm across the centre, not however attached to the .body. In spite of the bad deterioration of the surface there is evidence of advanced rendering of the anatomy. Fine work of the middle of the 4th century B.C., according to one opinion the forerunner of the famous Apoxyomenos of Lysippus. Found on the south slopes of the Acropolis before 1877. Height 0.49 m.

The room of Epidaurus is devoted exclusively to sculptures from the excavations in the sanctuary of Asklepios (1882 - 84).

The greater number come from the pediments of the temple of Asklepios. On the east was represented the capture of Troy, on the west the battle of the Amazons. According to a very important inscription relating to the building operations of the temple four sculptors were employed for the acroteria of the two sides and for the figures of the pediments: *Timotheos, Hektoridas, Theo...,* and a fourth whose name is not preserved. Within four years, eight months, and some days the building of the temple was completed (in the first decades of the 4th century B.C.). The sculptures of the temple, put together in recent years with many pieces which were transferred from the Museum of Epidaurus have changed aspects, radically creating astonishment by the daring innovations of the artists in the linking of the figures and have enriched our knowledge as regards the arrangement of the pediments.

3397. Torso of the figure of a woman, Nereid or Aura. Dressed in a diaphanous peplos, girded, she inclines toward the left, while she lifts the edge of her cloak with her left hand. She is seated on a dolphin (?). The back surface is well worked. The provenance of Epidaurus is uncertain and also the attribution of the poetic sculpture to the school of Timotheos. Beginning of the 4th century B.C. Height 0.60 m.

157. Acroterion of the temple of Asklepios. A beautiful woman, Nereid, Aura, or goddess, on a horse which emerges with its forefeet from the Ocean. The skillful pleating reveals the outline of her body. This, as well as her head, leans slightly toward the horse's neck. Hole for the application of the harness. Work of one of the principal sculptors of the temple. About 380 B.C. Height 0.78 m., width 0.66 m. (P l. 37).

156. From the same sculptor is the corresponding figure from the other corner of the pediment. The head is
missing. Height 0.74 m., width 0.67 m.

155. Statue of Nike (Victory), headless, who holds a bird.
She wears a diaphanous chiton and steps forward. Her
cloak behind is windblown around her wings (recently attached and thus her old name, Epione, has ceased to be
used). Slight turning toward the left breast. Skillful antithetic
spreading of the material. Central acroterion of the temple of Asklepios if not an independent offering. Height
0.85 m.

Below the window : Part of the wonderful roofing of
the Doric entablature from the Tholos or Thymele (hearth)
of Epidaurus (the circular building part of which is restored in the Museum there). The sima, the gutter, consisted
of meander decoration ; above, curling plants with stems,
with leaves and acanthus flowers. The acanthus grows out
from below palmettes. In the intervals lion heads with uneven surface, with open mouths and hollowed eyes. All the
foliage, strikingly chiaroscuro, reflects the restless spirit of
the period. 2nd half of the fourth century B.C. Height to
the apex of the palmette 0.53 m.

299. Statue of the goddess Hygeia, headless. She is
represented with her upper body bent forward, stepping
with her left leg upon a slight elevation, in front of which
is a snake. The other leg is drawn back, bent. She is dressed
in a light peplos with half her breast bare. The himation
falls on her raised leg and covers all the back producing
a richness of folds on the left side, while in front encircling
her right hand it casts a shadow. Excellent work probably
by the sculptor Timotheos, about 370 B.C. with influence
of the sculpture from the balustrade of the temple of Athena
Nike. Found in Epidaurus in 1884. Height 0.87 m. (Pl. 38).

1425. Heavy plaque with relief figures on three sides. Above is a very delicate Lesbian moulding (cyma reversa) and astragals. On the broad panel on the right Asklepios, bearded, is seated on a deep throne. He would have held the sceptre in his raised right hand. On the left in front of him a goddess, frontal. Behind her is spread the edge of the wing and the chlamys of a Nike who occupied the left narrow side. On the corresponding side to the right the figure of a woman, archaistic of the type of the Kore, probably Hebe, holds an oinochoe. By the hand of a competent artist about 370 B.C. The presence of the archaistic current at this early period is significant. Found in Epidaurus. The use of the plaque is uncertain. It may possibly have been an architectural member of some building or balustrade. Height 0.63 m., width above 1.07 m., below 0.94 m., depth 0.18 m.

From the western pediment. The battle of the Amazons :
136. Amazon rider, facing right, headless, wears a short chiton and boots; the chlamys falls behind her back. In her raised hand she brandished her spear above a warrior fallen under the raised front leg of her horse. It was very near the centre of the pediment if not at its axis. Height 0.90 m., width 0.81 m.

4492. Torso of a nude, dead young man, with the extended legs crossed. He is stretched toward the left above a rough surface, where there is thrown a garment of many folds probably his himation. The head (now missing) fell slightly tilted toward the back. It belonged probably to the left edge of the west pediment. Length 0.91 m., maximum height 0.30 m.

137. Body of an Amazon, mortally wounded, who falls from her horse. In the hole in her right breast would have been wedged the spear of the victorious warrior. The right

9

arm lifeless falls perpendicularly. Length 0.49 m., height
0.43 m. To the body of this Amazon would probably have
belonged the head no. **142**, with half-closed eyes. Height
0.11 m.

Group of a kneeling warrior who grasps the hair of a conquered Amazon (Only her head is preserved, which turns
back in agony). Height of the warrior 0.54 m., of the Amazon 0.63 m.

Figures from the eastern pediment. The sack of Troy :

146. Statue of a woman resting on her knees facing left.
The upper body is missing. The himation, with folds in deep
grooves, falls heavily concentrated above a small person on
the right who is being pulled back. It is uncertain whether
the name Hecuba is right for this Trojan woman. Height
0.50 m., width 0.48 m.

146a. The right section of the body of a Trojan woman,
attacking. Leaning back, on her knees, she probably raised
a·large axe above the body of a nude warrior who flees to
the right (there is preserved only his stretched right leg).
A similar subject known from a red figured hydria of the
painter Kleophrades in Naples. Of the same block are two
figures, the one behind the other. Height 0.66 m., width
0.52 m.

4642. The most astonishing of all the sculptures of the
temple is this composition of two figures from one piece
of marble : a woman who stands behind bends forward
to protect a little girl in front of her, kneeling. There is an
obvious attempt at depth; the upper body of the woman
turns antithetically toward the back. The work would have
been very near the centre, but to the left. The weathering of
the front figure is the greater. A work of powerful inspiration of one of the most important sculptors of the temple. Height 0.83 m., width 0.56 m.

144. The head of an old oriental, probably Priam, with a *tiara;* he opens his mouth in anguish. At the back traces of the marble which joined it with another figure.

162. The upper headless torso of a slender figured Nike. Above the spread right wing the edge of the himation is caught by the wind, while under the wing another part of the himation is curved below, with a magic effect of flexibility in the marble. An ethereal work with fabulous spirit, perhaps from the hand of Timotheos. Probably an acroterion or an independent offering in the shrine. Height 0.25 m.

173. A relief, votive (or architectural ?). Upon a cushioned chair Asklepios is seated facing right, his feet crossed on a footstool. His bare chest is 3/4 facing ; his face godlike. The palm of his left hand is open in benediction. A work in one of the leading sculptors of the pediment figures. About 380 B.C. (The head belongs to the relief, the opinion that it is alien is unsupported). Height of the old part 0.64 m., length without the restoration 0.47 m.

174. A relief, votive or architectural. On a rich throne, placed sideways a god is seated comfortably, facing right (Asklepios or Apollo), with chest bared and on his feet beautiful sandals. Holes on the head for attachment of the metal crown. The face is missing. The damage on the right cheek leaves it doubtful if the head was bearded. About 340 B.C., some decades later than no. 173, as shown by the oblique perspective in the setting of the throne and of the god. Height 0.63 m., width 0.70 m.

163. Lion head from a gutter of the temple of Asklepios. The elevation of the mane is without the dramatic chiaroscuro of the lion heads of the later tholos (in the same room below the window). About 370 B.C. Found at Epidaurus. Height about 0.23 m.

159 - 161 Three figures from the temple of Artemis at

Epidaurus : Victories who fly forward. The best preserved, no. 159, shows the type clearly. The bared right leg is slightly advanced. At the back the folds reveal the lower body, on the right with perpendicular direction, in waves on the left. The chiton is girded high below the breast, the neck long. The very graceful head is lengthened at the back by a thick coil of hair. No. 161 with folds more extended and somewhat flat would have been the central acroterion. They are carved with fresh feeling and advanced technique. In a known and accepted scheme the sculptor succeeded in inspiring an ethereal spirit and grace. End of the 4th century B.C. On the wall are the remains of a torso of a fourth Nike and two charming heads of similar figures. Height no. 159 0.80 m., no. 160 0.67 m., no. 161 0.70 m.

FIRST ROOM OF GRAVE MONUMENTS
OF THE 4th CENTURY B.C.

In the remaining rooms of grave monuments of the classical period there have been exhibited works of the 4th century. There is thus
completed the picture of this type, which begins in the Athens of the
5th century contemporary with the mature dramas of Sophocles
and disappears with the subjugation of the Athenian city at the end
of the 4th century.

With their forced inclusion in Museum rooms the grave monuments have lost the atmosphere which belongs to them. Whether in
the Kerameikos or outside other Athenian gates or in the cemeterie-
of the Attic demes, bathed in light, strewn with flowers, they receivs
ed the veneration of the passers - by.

One type which takes a novel development in the 4th century and
distinguishes these stelai from those of the 5th century is the large
grave shrine. Only a few are preserved whole because in the 19th
century certain archaeologists were concerned in preserving the relief
plaques and did not realize that the rest formed an inseparable part
of the monument. They were not concerned with saving the epistyle
with the pediment, which, supported on the side posts, threw a shadow upon the faces. Thus drown back into the depth of the shrine,
with a sort of remoteness from the spectator, they took on a distant
holiness.

Reliefs of the 4th century with three or four people show the need
for stressing the unity of the family. The dead are represented in the
warmth of their own people and it is difficult to distinguish the living from the dead ; the implications become delicate, the identification very often remains problematical.

In these rooms also the variety of grave monuments is impressive. Very high stelai crowned with palmettes; statues of mourning
Sirens, young women seated on rocks; goats, symbols of Dionysos, the
god of souls. One must imagine most of them placed in front of shrines,
as many as were not cornices for stelai. Above the tombs of the un-
married young — young men or girls — were placed loutrophoroi of
marble. Among the grave lekythoi a large example with the figure
of the priest Pantaleon shows that important artists often elevated the
figures into the heroic sphere.

It is not, however, only such monuments as these which move us. The series of crude works which were carved by modest marble-workers wrench the heart strings. Whether they are independent of known works or not, they express a deep human and sensitive bitterness over an unjust destiny.

Parallel with compositions with many people those with two people and also flourish, showing the tragic isolation of the consecrated dead, as in the shrine of Aristonautes; here the principal and only figure is of the lost warrior. It is a reflection of the confusion of souls at the irreparable mystery of death. In the stelai of the 5th century we saw it expressed with less dramatic effect, with bitter serenity.

The new sentiments in the 4th century are as usual expressed by the stylistic form : A new relation of the figures with the architectural frame, the gradual move toward the plastic rounding of the figures, toward the representation of large-scale, revered figures in front of the surface of the back ground, the alternation of poses, the search for new rhythms of the body as well as the study of its relation to the dress—all these things are bound up with the spiritual drama which the sculptors of the fourth century revealed, giving to the white marble new vibrations of life, a new reflection of death.

751. Grave stele of Alkias of Phocis, with pediment. The name on the epistyle. A hoplite, facing left, steps over a nude dead body of a young man stretched on a rock. The long chlamys of the former is drawn firmly down below the shield. Colours emphasize the surface as well as the two bands which stand out plastically, hanging like a frame for the warrior. Found at Corinth, it is a work of a local sculptor of the end of the fifth century B.C. The subject has an ostentatious rhetorical provincialism. Height 0.74 m., width 0.50 m.

2583. Statue of a mourning Siren. Standing with feet forward she has turned back both body and face, while her hands pull her hair in mourning. On her face an expression of deep grief. Behind are spread the wings which would have been shown with colour. Her tail is joined with the plinth. Found in the Kerameikos. Height 1.17 m.

818. Grave stele with simple pediment. A young woman is comfortably seated on a chair looking left. In the second use of the stele the name has been carved on the epistyle. At that time the figure of the child standing in front of her was chiselled off, as well as the bird which she offered in her right hand, probably the head - dress was also much altered. Found at Thespiae. By the hand of a local sculptor about 410 B.C. It copies a well-known prototype, propably Pheidian. Height 1.50 m., width 0.94 m.

829. Stele, long and narrow, of a young hunter. He was represented nude with head bent toward his dog. Found at Thespiae in 1814. Coarse work of the beginning of the 4th century, from Boeotian limestone, copy of a good Ionian original. Height total 1.75 m., width 0.75 m.

817. Grave stele of a poetess (?). A young woman is seated on a stool facing left, leaning on her arm which, stretched vertically, closes the composition. Under the stool is a pyxis with two cylindrical books. Graceful footstool. A nude boy (the upper part of his body missing) raises his hand toward the woman. The high girding of her diaphanous chiton, her delicate proportions place the work at the end of the 4th century B.C. Found at Thespiae in 1869. From local limestone by the hand of a Boeotian sculptor. The whole graceful figure of the young woman whom the cylinders characterize as a poetess. suggests an Attic original. Height 1.47 m., width 1 m.

770. The upper part of a grave stele. The pediment is missing. Confined in the centre in a closed square is a relief of a lion, standing, facing right, with a rich mane. Two rosettes above, higher the name of the deceased : *Leon Sinopeus*. About 370 B.C. The lion, an allegory of the name, shows likewise the bravery of the young man. Found in Attica in 1826. Height 0.53 m., width 0.44 m.

806. The upper part of a long narrow grave stele, with relief on the epikranium : two goats confronted with horns mingled, a kantharos in the centre. Under the moulding two rosettes in relief; higher up is carved the name of the deceased : *Dionysios Ikarios*. Middle of the 4th century B.C. Found in Athens. Height of the old part 1.02 m.

1688. Heavy plaque, from the roof of a grave monument (of an unusual type in Attica). Two triglyphs and a central metope with three figures in relief : Two women seated facing one another. The left with bowed head, covered with himation. In the middle a standing figure (male ?) facing right with bowed head. The face is damaged. First half of the 4th century B.C. Found in 1892 in Athens, near the Tower of the Winds. Length with the plinth 0.61, length 1.16 m.

3868. Lion from a grave monument, with a rectangular plinth. His front legs extended, he bends his body, the head turned toward the spectator. The mouth is open, the mane shown by tongues of flame pattern. Work of a good sculptor, it had been thoughtfully planned; it has handsome curves, some variety in the formation of the planes of the body in front and careful carving. Beginning of the 4th century B.C. Found in Attica in 1940. Height of the plinth 0.61 m., length 1.16 m.

772. Small grave stele of a priest. Central palmette with many petals and two halves at the ends. Standing facing right in a hollowed plane the priest wears an ungirded chiton with short sleeves and holds in his right hand the sacrificial knife. His name is carved on the bare surface above : *Simon Myrrhinousios :* First half of the 4th century B. C. Found in 1858 in Athens (Stadium Street). Height 0.64 m.

731. Large grave stele, once in the form of a shrine. On the right, part of the body of a hoplite is preserved, facing left. He has his hand on the head of a child. At the back in low relief, the father wearing a himation, leaning on his staff, looks at his son. The face, influenced by portraits of the philosophers, is suffused with deep sorrow. About 340 B.C. One of the good products of the period, badly preserved. Found on Salamis. Height 1.76 m., width 1.02 m.

3416 - 17. Two slabs from the covering of the square base of a grave monument, joined. No. 3416, a dog, a greyhound, runs toward the left. No. 3417, a similar dog tracks footsteps. Probably of the middle of the 4th century. Found on Salamis in 1896. Height 0.48 m., width 0.66 - 0.77 m.

870. The « stele of the farewell », once in the form of a shrine. On the left, seated on a stool, a woman turns to face another young woman, standing opposite, and extends her right arm, which the other holds to her breast with her left hand. On the left, in a second plane, behind the seated woman, the upper body of a little girl who looks at the standing woman. By her feet is a bird. The appearance of the second woman with head covered by her himation suggests that this is the deceased. However, the exaggerated expression of the seated woman indicates that she is the mistress of the tomb. The full bodies, the diagonal arrangement of the stool and the footstool, the plastic fulness of the figures, date this work of a sensitive and capable sculptor to the years after the middle of the 4th century. It is not, however, certain that this is the famous original, the source of several contemporary repetitions which are preserved. (See the adjacent lekythos no. 3486). Found in 1882 in Athens. Height 1.70 m., width 1.20 m. (Pl. 40 a).

3486. Small marble lekythos of Polystrate. The relief scene has the same theme as the adjacent large stele no.

870. The name above the figures : *Polystrate* and (in the second row) *Paronymion Dennanis*. Found in Athens in 1927. Height of the old part 0.73 m.

900. Small, simple grave stele of Tito, from Samos, with pediment. The figure, seated on a chair facing left, bows her head. She is enclosed in a hollow square. Higher on the relief, her name. Found in Piraeus. Height 0.84 m., width 0.31 m.

1022. Grave stele, very tall, with floral roofing. The palmette concave with the edges of the petals without outlines, while in the lower part the spirals and acanthus are in high relief. On the upper part of the plaque two rosettes in relief, a little higher below the moulding the name of the deceased : *Daisias Euthiou Alaieus*. Below the two rosettes, in five successive rows, were carved later the names of his two sons, Euthias and Euthykritos. On the remaining bare part of the stele were painted red bands. About 340 B.C. Found at Brauron (Attica). Height 3.21 m.

869. The « stele of the Ilissos ». A 'large grave stele, of a young hunter, once in the form of a shrine. On the left a young man, nude, with legs crossed, standing, buttocks resting against a low column, looks forward beyond the spectator. He holds in his hand what is probably a stick. On the right, standing, a man with rich beard, wearing a himation, leans on his staff gazing at his son with an expression of deep sorrow. Below the legs of the young man his greyhound is tracking the ground. On the stairway above a small slave half asleep rests his face on his knee. A work of an important, sensitive sculptor, possibly of the sculptor Skopas himself or someone of his rank. About 340 B.C. There are preserved certain replicas of the subject which must have had much fame. (The most complete is the adjacent, no. 871). Found in the bed of the Ilissos in 1874.

Height 1.68 m., width below 1.10 m. (without the restoration) (Pl. 39).

871. Grave stele, large, once in the form of a shrine. On the left a bearded man facing right looks at a young man facing him who leans his head on his right hand, with mournful expression. Behind him a small slave seated on the ground. A crude work of about 340 B.C., a free echo of the gleaming adjacent original, no. 869. The marble worker of no. 871 was not inspired beyond a conventional version expressed by external means. Found in 1840 in the Kerameikos. Height 1.62 m., width 0.80 m.

3460. Plaque from the base of a large grave monument with moulding,. once painted. A greyhound runs toward the right, his front legs upright and his head raised. Behind him is preserved the lowered head and part of the body of a second dog who is running in the same direction. Excellent work of unusual plastic force. Found in Piraeus. Second half of the 4th century B.C. Length 0.94 m., height of the old part 0.41 m.

814. Grave lekythos with relief decoration. In the centre on a simple stool is seated a woman facing right, who holds an open pyxis (?). Her feet are on a high footstool. Opposite are two standing figures, a woman and a youth in a himation. Behind her the servant, dressed in a sleeved chiton, holds a baby in her arms. Above the head of the seated woman the names are carved : *Phano - Kallipis*. Good work about 420 B.C. Found on Salamis. Height of the old part 1.16 m.

826. Large grave stele with low pediment, with marked projection. In high relief the two standing figures confronted : a woman with full body, her himation thrown behind her head, receives a man. Her open left palm fills the centre of the plaque with the promise of a meeting. Found in 1830 on Salamis. Somewhat provincial, of about 350 B.C., the stele is noteworthy, however, for the plastic fulness of the figures. Height 2.05 m., width 1.20 m.

898. Small grave stele of Telesias, with pediment. On the left, a youth, nude, holds in his left hand a rabbit. His cloak hangs from his left arm. Facing him a small nude slave raises his head toward his master. The name of the deceased carved on the epistyle. First half of the 4th century B.C. It was in the Piraeus Museum until 1888. Height 0.84 m., width 0.40 m.

743. Grave stele of Damasistrate, with pediment. The name on the epistyle. Seated on a throne, facing left, the young woman receives the standing man. In the background a woman looking down. Standing on the left a slave girl, dressed in the barbaric sleeved dress, leans against the support of the throne. Mediocre, dependent work diffused with noble sorrow. Found in 1838 in Piraeus. Height 1.12 m., width 0.77 m.

4498. Small marble lekythos, inserted in a tetragonal base. Four relief figures on the body of the lekythos. On the three sides of the base relief figures, the most significant is on the right broad side : a young female figure, standing facing left, dressed in the sleeved peplos of actors bends her head toward a mask (of a tragic heroine ?) which she holds in her right hand. Good small work of the beginning of the 4th century B.C. Found in 1961 at Vari in Attica. Total height 0.83 m., height of the lekythos 0.556 m.

896. Grave stele, rectangular. It represents a loutrophoros with relief figures on the horizontal section : On the right a girl decorates with a fillet the handle of a loutrophoros. On the left another girl advances, wrapped in a himation, behind her a third female figure. On the pediment a mourning Siren with wings skillfully spread. About

360 B.C. Found in Attica in 1877. Height 1.61 m., width 0.51 m.

774. A sepulchral Siren mourns the deceased, holding a primitive lyre (a turtle shell). The raised wings frame her face. Her feet below are missing. Middle of the 4th century B.C. Found in the Kerameikos in 1863. Height 0.83 m.

744. Acroterion with curves, of the grave stele of a girl. In front of a climbing leaf pattern in high relief (stylized spirals) a young woman advances upright toward the right, (in 3/4 view) with polos on her head, holding in her lowered hands the edges of her windblown cloak. Behind and above her head the palmette which sprouts high from the spirals. It is a symbolic picture of the apotheosized dead girl in the verdant, airy plains of the Ocean. About 350 B.C. Found at Trachones in Attica. Height 0.85 m., width 0.46 m.

722. Grave stele of a young mother, Archestrate, with pediment. She is seated on a stool, facing left, and takes with her right hand some object from the pyxis which the girl standing, facing her, holds. Over the right knee of the dead girl appears the head and arm of a small boy who holds a bird. A touching simple work of a good marble worker about 370 B.C. Simple proportions of the bodies. Epigram on the epistyle. Found in 1830 in Attica. Height 1.40 m., width 0.95 m.

3378. The upper part of a large grave stele of Leon and Leontios, with pediment. On the left the head of a beautiful youth with an expression of surpassing rapture. On the right the upper body of a bearded man. It is not certain whether both figures are shown standing. The unusual open space above their heads gives to the scene an eloquent simplicity. About 360 B.C. Found in Athens in 1915. Height 1 m., width 1 m.

815. Marble lekythos with relief representation. A seated woman in the centre receives a young warrior who stands facing her. Behind him a standing woman, on the left another holds in her left hand a basket with offerings and fillets. The subject has parallels only on painted lekythoi. About 370 B.C. Found probably in Athens. Known since 1860. Height 0.94 m.

941. Small grave stele with rounded roofing, where there are two delicate antithetic half-palmettes. Under the carved cornice the name of the deceased : *Aristogeiton Nikiou Alopekethen.* Lower down rosettes and an artistic, graceful loutrophoros, with bands around the neck. Unknown provenance. About 350 B.C. Height 0.94 m.

SECOND ROOM OF GRAVE MONUMENTS
OF THE 4th CENTURY B.C.

1055. The grave lekythos of Theophante who, seated in the centre on a stool, breathes her last breath. On the left a woman restrains her. She has placed her left arm on the hand of her sorrowing husband. Her name is above the relief. According to one well-founded opinion it represented a woman who died in child birth. (See the adjacent stele no. 749). Found probably in the Kerameikos. Height of the old part 0.78 m.

749. Grave stele, with pediment. The subject similar to the adjacent no. 1055 — the death of a young woman (here resting on a couch) — has more movement, a fact which confirms its dependence on a painted prototype. On the flat open surface below the pediment the names : *Plaggon Tolmidou Plataike. Tolmides Plataieus.* Found at Oropos. Height 0.75 m., width 0.50 m.

2546. Neck of a loutrophoros with relief decoration. High, above the acanthus, stands a mourning Siren. The outlines of the spiral handles coil in graceful curves.Found in Athens in 1903. Height 0.51 m., width 0.44 m.

832. Large grave stele, formerly in the form of a shrine. On the left a young woman seated on a stool receives another tall figure who stands in front of her, with bowed head, covered by her himation. In the background in low relief a bearded man, at the back a small slave girl with the barbaric sleeved chiton leans her head on her left hand. An exceptional work of a sensitive artist. Exceptionally rapt expression of the seated deceased woman. Found in Athens. According to Conze (in his no. 337) the pediment of the stele was found in a private house and had on its epistyle the names of the man and his wife; only the second is well preserved : *Philino Thoukritou Phlyeos*. About 340 B. C. Brought to the National Museum in 1889. Height 1.80 m., length 1.22 m.

823 - 824. Two statues of Scythian bowmen, headless. They wear trousers and the sleeved chiton, girded, and are on their knees antithetically, each with one leg. No. 823, the better preserved with a small part of the plinth, has placed his right hand toward the sheath of his bow. They would have decorated the facade of a large grave shrine of an officer (the Scythians formed the police of Athens). According to one opinion they belonged to the tomb of Lysimachides of Acharnae. 2nd half of the 4th century B.C. Found in the Dipylon in 1836. No. 823 height 0.74 m., no. 824 height 0.70 m.

1896. Small grave stele of a dancer, with low pediment. She is shown full-face with diaphanous chiton, holding the castanets in her hands. On the left a small boy wearing a himation raises toward her his right hand in which he holds a bird, and he has another similar one in his lowered left hand. Light Attic work of the middle of the 4th century B.C. Found, probably, in Athens. Height 0.78 m.

966. Plaque from a large grave shrine. The figure in high relief. An elderly woman with short hair, flowing as far as her throat, standing facing left holds the edge of her himation in her right hand. Work of a capable artist, worthy of attention for his effort to show the features of her face as well as the rendering of the matriarchal figure. Found in 1891 in the Kerameikos. Height 2.07 m., width 0.68 m., depth of the plaque 0.36 m. (there remained only 0.65 m. after the woman was carved). Another two plaques of the samaftcr the size would hava belonged to the monument.

888. Section of a small grave stele with frame. A nude

young athlete in low relief, looking down, holds a strygil in his right hand while he raises the other above his head. His weight would have been on the right leg. Delicate technique of the middle of the 4th century B.C. The subject is inspired by a pre - Lysippean statue. Found in Piraeus in 1836. Height 0.46 m., width 0.23 m.

1488. Grave stele with low pediment. According to a bilingual inscription, Greek and Phoenician, it was placed on the tomb of one Antipater son of Aphrodisios of Askalon from Sidonios Domsalon son of Domanios. Above the inscription is a small and unskilled relief in a square compartment. On a bed the deceased and on the left a lion which rises to tear him to pieces. A man hastens to defend him. At the back is drawn the prow of a ship. The theme unique among the Attic grave monuments. First half of the 4th century B.C. Found in the Kerameikos in 1861. Height 1.38 m.

938. The upper part of the relief on the neck of a loutrophoros. Under the spirals two confronted young men, nude, support them with one hand (Zephyrs ?). They would have stood on an acanthus. Found probably in Piraeus. Height 0.27 m., width about 0.28 m.

3574. Grave monument of a dog looking right, in a pose of rest, with its plinth. The back surface unworked, it would have stood in front of a funeral shrine. Mediocre work of the 2nd half of the 4th century B.C. Found in Piraeus in in 1925. Height 0.53 m., width 0.80 m.

379. Head of a bearded man from a sepulchral shrine. His hair falls around his face, thick, freely rendered, as is also his beard. The formation of his face has been delicately rendered. Good Attic work of about 340 B.C. Found in Attica. Height 0.32 m., width 0.27-0.28 m.

834. Large grave stele of a warrior, once in the form of a shrine. The figure in noticeably high relief. A warrior with thorax is represented full face, with legs crossed. He rests his left hand on the helmet which a nude slave is offering him, the other hand on his hip. Below at the back his shield. His gaze is exaggeratedly directed into the distance. A good work of this kind of about 340 B.C. In the original — some statue — there would have been better balance ; the figure would have been supported with the left hand on a short column. Found at Eleusis in 1888. Height 1.66, m. width 0.92 m.

4763. Grave monument of a dog, a greyhound. Seated resting on his back legs (there is preserved there a part of the plinth as well) the front legs straight. The long stretched neck which is slightly inclined toward the front and the head with ears raised contributes to the lively impression. Work of a good sculptor as the undulation in the plasticity of the anatomy demonstrates. Bad deterioration of the surface. Found in Attica. Height 0.77 m., width 0.60 m.

3552. Small head of an elderly woman, covered with a himation. From a grave monument. Good example of the influence of portrait sculpture on grave monuments. Found in 1892 in Athens. Height 0.19 m.

873. Part of a small grave stele. There is preserved the body of a loutrophoros with simple relief scenes of the palaistra. In the centre a young man nude raises his right leg ; on his knee there is a ball. He has drawn back his right arm and with his hand clasps the left wrist. Behind on the right a low column on which there is a folded chlamys. On the left a small nude slave holds an aryballos and a strygil. Delicate technique. Middle of the 4th century B.C. Found in Piraeus in 1836. Height 0.44 m., width 0.335 m.

3716. The « radiant monument ». Large grave stele of a woman, once in the form of a shrine. It lacks the upper part with the heads of the two figures, as well as certain parts of the plaque below on the left. The deceased, seated on a stool, occupies all of the central part of the plaque, her breast at the top. She raises in her right hand the edge of the himation which she wraps so that it falls in many folds — all « froth and foam » at the centre of her body. Between her legs is her left hand, heavy but beautiful. On the right a standing woman holds a pyxis obliquely in front of her breast. On the left is preserved the head of a little slave with her hair bound in a net. She wears the barbaric sleeved chiton. The robust principal central figure, an un-usual one on grave monuments, reflects the magnitude of the original (the Hera of the Parthenon frieze). There is here the divine portrait of the heroized woman. A splendid work of a noteworthy sculptor of about 380 B.C. Found pro-bably in Attica. Restored. Height of the ancient part 1.375 m., width 1.25 m. (Pl. 40 b).

188. The « head from Lerna ». The neck is also preser-ved. Head of a woman, full face, flat behind. It belonged probably to the central figure of a monument which would have been a local echo of Attic grave shrines. Work of an Argive sculptor — which we deduce from the studied portrayal of the hair and the stiffness of the pose — it is not without a transcendent elevation. Second half of the 4th century B.C. Found at Argive Lerna. Until 1888 it was in the Museum at Argos. Height 0.38 m.

737. A large grave monument of the family of Pro-kleides, in the form of a shrine with pediment. On the right, standing facing his father who is seated on a chair, is a young man, a bearded warrior with chiton and thorax who gives his hand to his father. These two figures in high relief, while in the background, in lower relief, the mother stands full face. The names are carved on the epistyle. Aside from the three figures, Prokleides, Archippe, and Prokles, there is a second Prokleides. The base is ancient, from Hymettus marble. About 330 B.C. Found in the Kerameikos in 1861. Height of the relief 1.80 m., length 1.30 m., height of the base 0.44 m., width 2.25 m.

825. Statue of a young servant seated on the ground, in mournful pose. The head is missing. She wears a girded peplos and her legs are crossed. She supports her head on her right hand. Found in Athens in 1887 (Stadium Street). It would have been set in front of one of the large monuments of the middle of the 4th century B.C. A contemporary replica of this important work was on a tomb at Acharnae (Menidi) the Museum of Berlin ; the head is also preserved) On this there is missing the artistic pleating which was combined, in the original in the National Museum, with an effect of unusual plastic fulness. Height 0.83 m., depth. 0.77 - 0.78 m.

819. Grave stele of a young mother once in the form of a shrine. The young woman seated on a rich throne facing left, puts her hand on a pyxis which is on her lap. Facing her a sorrowful woman. The dead woman looks high beyond her with other - world abstraction. In the background between them a girl holds a baby in a peaked cap. On the right are traces of the body of a slave who leans in sorrow against the throne support. The rich throne shows the need to heroize this woman, unjustly dead (in child birth ?). A work of the middle of the 4th century which expresses a sense of unbearable grief. Found in Piraeus in 1837. Height 1.32 m., width 0.95 m.

954. Grave loutrophoros, in relief. All the upper part and the base are missing. Superb delicacy of the light relief, of the rich decoration : fluted stripes which extend to the shoulder, above them a double plait. Between and below the handles sprout palmettes of acanthus. The very delicate, airy petals of the palmettes and the whole technique support a date about 320 B. C. On each side of the central handle are distinguished the extremities of the two symbolic figures (otherwise free standing) treading on acanthus leaves. Found probably in Athens. Height of the ancient part 1.15 m.

3691. Grave stele of Kephisokritos and of his daughter Stratyllis in the form of a shrine with horizontal cornice. On the left, seated on a chair, the venerable father receives the standing girl facing him. The names carved on the epistyle. About 340 B.C. Found in Athens in 1930. Height 1.48 m.

3605. Grave stele with low epistyle and cornice. Two confronted figures, a seated woman and a standing man clasp hands. Between them in the background, in low relief, two standing figures, full face, a woman and a man. A lifeless, clumsy work of a marble sculptor, dependent on better originals. (The adjacent large stele of Alexos, no. 2574, shows that the best sculptors of such stelai knew how to avoid the heaviness of the epistyle immediately above the heads of the figures). Found in 1922 in Attica. Height 1.45 m., width 1.15 m.

1006. Part of a large grave shrine. Of the finished relief there is preserved the head and shoulder of a woman, at 3/4 toward the right. She is covered with a himation the edge of which is held in the fingers of her right hand. The other — world expression on her face shows that she is the dead woman. When complete it would have been an impressive monument, of about 350 B.C. Found in the Kerameikos. Height 0.55 m.

901. Small grave stele, with simple horizontal moulding and narrow epistyle. A young woman, Selino, seated on a chair, facing the right, holds in her left hand a mirror, and with the other greets a girl standing in front of her

(she wears a peplos with unusually long overfold) who holds a small child by the hand. Above, the names *Selino, Niko, Mynnake*. A simple, pleasing work about 370 B. C. Found in 1879 in Athens. Height 0.74 m., width 0.28 m.

193. Head of a mourning Siren, formerly inserted in a statue, with marked expression of grief. Abundant hair covers her forehead and falls to her shoulders, her mouth is half open. About 320 B.C. Found in the Kerameikos. Height 0.36 m.

775. Sepulchral Siren. Standing on her front legs she holds in her left hand a lyre in the form of a tortoise shell, in the other the plectrum, in front of her breast. Her wings are missing and her feet below with the plinth. Second half of the 4th century B.C. Found in the Kerameikos. Height of the old part 1.02 m.

2574. A large memorial monument of the family of Alexos from Sounion, in the form of a shrine with horizontal cornice. The whole of this is preserved, as well as a plaque with a figure in high relief : Alexos facing right, bends forward leaning with his left elbow on his staff. On the two plaques which are missing were represented: in front, seated probably facing right, his wife, Philoumene ; Stratokles, his son, standing facing him in « welcome », while between them in low relief full face, was the servant Phanostrate. The names are carved on the epistyle (Ionic type with three horizontal compartments). Imposing work of an important sculptor about 320 B.C. Found in 1902 in Athens. For the first time now in the new exhibition the figure has been joined with its radiant cornice which has been brought out of store and established in its original position. Total height 2.20 m., height of the relief plaque 1.80 m., width of the cornice above about 2.45 m., width of the plaque 0.63 m.

3619. Grave monument of two separate sections. Below, a round floral column and three large palmettes which rest on acanthus leaves. At the apex stands a large marble cauldron with four griffins around and above it. Perpendicular rows of relief stripes support the body of the cauldron, which are interrupted by a horizontal plaited band. The griffins are modern, of plaster, in the positions where there were traces. A rare work of good quality about 340 B.C. Found in Athens in 1926. Total height 1.82 m., height of the column (as far as the central petals) 0.88 m.

It is preferable not to interrupt the visit to the grave monuments but to leave going into the small rooms of votive reliefs until later after one has finished viewing the last grave monuments of the 4th century B.C.

2244. Head of a woman from a large grave stele. Slightly bowed, she is covered with the himation the edge of which she held with her left hand. From her deeply diffused sorrow and her isolation we conclude that she is the deceased. Provenance unknown. Height 0.32 m., width 0.36 m.

4496. The left side plaque of a large grave shrine. In low relief a slave girl with a short mourning hair-cut. She wears the barbaric sleeved chiton and a peplos with a long overfold ; she brings her lefth and toward her face directing her inconsolable eyes toward the distant background. The whole monument would have been the work of an important artist of the 2nd half of the 4th century B.C. Found in Attica in 1957. Height 1.82 m., width 0.55 m. (Pl. 50a).

Opposite : **3694**. The right doorpost of a grave monument. In somewhat low relief a young slave facing left holds the strigil and aryballos of his master. The earlier half of the 4th century B. C. Found in Athens. Height 1.66 m., width 0.46 m.

3488. Head, bearded, full face, fragment of a grave stele. Worthy of attention for its attempt at a portrait rendering of the face. Middle of the 4th century B.C. Found in Athens about 1924. Height 0.18 m.

576 - 577. Two bearded heads from a large grave shrine. No. 576 had a marked turning towards the left ; in no. 577 is the diffused, unrestrained sorrow of death. Found at Rhamnous in Attica in 1879, it probably belonged to a grave stele which is still there. The surface of both much eaten by salt. 2nd half of the 4th century B.C. See the adjacent stele no. 833.

820. Grave stele of a young woman, with pediment. Seated on a stool with face nearly frontal. Opposite, another young woman who sorrowfully bends her head (covered with himation) in the direction of the deceased, leaning slightly on her hand. The lower part of the stele is missing. About 330 B. C., with the isolation of the two figures customary for this period. Found in Athens. Height 1.55 m., width 1.09 m.

833. Large grave stele, once in the form of a shrine. In high relief two standing figures confronted in « welcome », looking at one another. On the left a bearded man, on the right a slender young woman, inspired by Praxitelean statues of goddesses. The arrangement of the hair, drawn together on the top of her head reveals her delicate neck. The instability of the crossed legs of the facing man is due to his leaning on his staff under his left armpit. By the same sculptor are the adjacent heads 'no. 576-577. 2nd half of the 4th century B.C. Found in 1879 at Rhamnous in Attica. Height 1.81 m., width 1.10 m.

738. The grave shrine of Aristonautes. Shaded by the epistyle and the pediment, in high relief in front of the plaque is portrayed the greater part of the body of a young warrior, deceased, who appears in an aggressive pose. He is dressed in a chiton and thorax, wears a pointed helmet and holds a shield ; in his right hand (missing) he would have held a spear or sword. Behind his body is his windblown cloak. His face is turned forward and his deep eyes gaze beyond the spectator. The left leg, in the round, is bent and rests upon the slightly elevated ground, while, above, the body is joined to the shield (the scheme antithetic to that of the other side). A metal crown would have been attached by the three holes in the helmet above his forehead. On the epistyle the name : *Aristonautes Archenautou Alaieus.* Half of the high, heavy base of the shrine is ancient. This famous monument found in 1864 in the Kerameikos is the work of a great sculptor. The creator infused into a known form a new dramatic emotion, the isolation of death, rendered the portrait with a novel plastic power. The carving of the folds of the chiton and himation is combined with painted details.The blue colour of the background enhanced the apparent immateriality of the heroized figure. About 310 B. C. Total height with the base 2.91 m., without the base 2.48 m., height of the figure 2 m., width below to the beginning of the doorway 1.55 m.

1005. The « last Attic grave relief ». Plaque from a shrine. There is preserved a standing woman, full face (the head missing) in moderately high relief, matriarchal. It is a faithful replica of some famous statue of Praxitelean technique. The type known from many later copies as the « tall woman from Herculaneum ». The carving good and lifelike (note the characteristic fluid folds of the chiton). The whole monument of a large type would have been the work of an exceptional sculptor with its eclectic arrangement of the figures. For the type of the head see the adjacent statue no. 779. Found in the Kerameikos. It is one of the last Attic monuments before the prohibitive law of 307 B.C. Height 1.89 m., width 0.82 m.

803 - 804. Two sepulchral lions, the one facing left, the other antithetical. With a slight bending of the head which he turns forward, each one holds under his feet the head of a calf. The rays of the mane formed by the use of the drill. Plastic variations in the body formation. Found in the Kerameikos in 1870. According to an old opinion they were placed antithetically at the corners of the base of the

tomb of Dionysios Kollyteus. No 803 : Height 0.62 m. width
1.06 m.; no 804 : Height 0.64 m., width 1.04 m.

2594. Small painted stele of a « Metic » (alien), with
moulding and epistyle (preserved on it is the green colour).
The figure of a young man standing facing right, outlined
in red. Above, the name *Tibeios Tianos*. Probably about 400
B.C. Found in Attica. Height 0.34 m., width 0.249 m.

779. The upper body of a woman from a grave monument (for the type see the adjacent stele no. 1005), unfinished. The glance, without direction. The whole work,
perhaps even a copy, has a Hellenistic atmosphere in the
carving. Found òn Rheneia. Height 0.56 m.

4464. Large relief. It consists of two plaques, joined at the
edges only (« anathyrosis »). Covering almost all of the surface facing right is a heavy horse which raises its left front leg.
On its back, is the skin of a panther the head of which with
closed eyes covers the chest of the horse. At the right, behind,
in a second plane, a dark young man (negro), a groom, raises
a whip with his right hand, with the other he offers to the
mouth of the horse an indeterminate red object. He wears
a short chiton and boots, his hair curly. Traces of a painted
helmet above the back of the horse. The chest and the head
(relatively small) of the horse, as well as the front legs
are in high relief. Colour is preserved - black on the face and
arms of the groom, red in the hair and elsewhere. Traces
of green in the mane of the horse and perpendicularly on
the left edge. Excellent work, unique, of a great artist.
Of great imagination, almost divine the portrait of the horse. The chronology is debateable. The relief, transitional
toward the early Hellenistic technique, yet connected with
the rendering of the last of the grave stelai; it should be
dated about 300 B.C. or immediately afterwards. It probably
formed the embellishment of the base of a statue of some

officer (Macedonian ?). The position of another plaque with
the end of the horse's tail is problematical. Found in Athens,
near and south of the Larisa station in 1948. Total height
2 m., length of the plaque on the left 1 m., of the other
with the front body 0.90 m., whole width 1.90 m., thickness
of the plaque 0.06 m., greatest thickness with the relief 0.33
m., least thickness 0.24 m. (Pl. 49).

1283. Side door jamb of a large grave shrine. In low relief a small slave full face, with barbaric dress, with her hands
clasped low. Hymettos marble. A work well planned, about
320 B.C. Found at Rhamnous. Height 1.75 m., width 0.51 m.
(Pl. 50 b).

1863. Grave stele f Agnostrate, daughter of Theodotos
(the names on the epistyle) in the form of a simple shrine.
On the left, beside the girl, in low relief a loutrophoros with
two confronted figures, Agnostrate and Theodoros (her
brother). Modest, somewhat empty work, about 330 B.C.
Found in Athens in 1896. Height 1.31 m., width 0.70 m.

1299. The upper part of a rectangular grave stele. Decoration in relief. A palmette above the acanthus. Near are
two standing goats with « butting horns ». Below, the inscription : *Epi Paramono* with letters which support a date
in the 2nd century B.C. Found in the Megarid. An example of the survival of the Attic style of the 4th century outside of Attica. Spiritless the floral conception, the carving
dry. Height 0.45 m., width 0.48 m.

1957. Part of an Attic grave stele of Demagora (the name on the epistyle) in the form of a shrine with pediment.
On an elegant throne the deceased is seated facing left,with
the upper body turned forward. Her himation covers her
head also. On the right standing behind her a young maid
servant with head full face. The expression of her face has
a certain emptiness which prevailed at the end of the 4th

century B.C. Found at Keratea in Attica. Height 1.44 m.

805. Covering of a grave monument. Two goats (in the round), with butting horns, rise from each side of a column. Good rendering of the heads and of the hair in both views, as well as in the plastic moulding. End of the 4th century B.C. Unknown provenance. Height of the ancient part 0.75 m., width 1 m.

709. Grave statue of a woman, with its plinth. She is dressed in chiton and himation, one edge of which she holds in her left hand. The other hand supports her head, covered with her himation. The rendering of the folds shows imagination and artistry. End of the 4th century B.C. Unknown provenance. Height 1.55 m.

943. High palmette finial of a rectangular grave stele. In front (the background, once blue, is restored) appears a foliate windblown decoration, full of sunshine : above spirals, twisted stems each supporting antithetic half - palmettes ; behind, another larger palmette ; both palmettes lean over toward the centre. One of the principal examples of the febrile decoration of the Attic stelai at the end of the 4th century B.C. Found in Athens in 1888. Height 1.40 m., width of the ancient part 0.70 m.

2728. The upper body of a large grave statue of an unknown oriental (Persian ?). He wears the sleeved chiton and the Median cloak. On his neck are the traces of the *tiara* which covered the inserted head (not preserved). The work of a capable sculptor of about 320 B.C. The pleating is flat, to show the thickness of the material. The back view is smooth. Found in 1908 in the Kerameikos. Height 1.04 m.

1482. Large rectangular decree inscription, with relief on the upper part, in the form of a shrine. The figures in the background. On the left Athena, in the centre the Demos of the Athenians (or Zeus Soter) receives a man. At the back a small groom pulls a horse by the reins. Dated from the name of the archon Euphron to 323 - 318 B.C. Found in the ancient Agora of Athens. Characteristic of the period is the unbending, curveless pose (copied from a known statue), as well as the shadows of the figures. Total height 2.40 m., height of the relief 0.60 m.

1471. Large decree stele with relief on the uppermost part. According to the lengthy inscription the three sons of King Leukon of the Cimmerian Bosporos, in 347 - 6 B.C. were honoured in this decree by the Athenians, on the occasion of a treaty exempting them from the corn tax. On the square relief the three Bosporites are wearing himatia, two seated facing right, the third standing facing them. The heads are missing. Slanting perspective of the throne and the footstools. Found near the harbour of Piraeus. Total height 2.12 m., width 0.63 m., height of the relief 0.50 m., length 0.50 m.

2948. The upper left part of a decree relief, in the form of a shrine. Four-horse chariot facing right with charioteer and a woman. Of the inscription below there is preserved one *R*. About the middle of the 4th century B.C. Found possibly in Athens. Height of the ancient part 0.40 m., width 0.32 m. Unusually heavy, the plaque has a thickness of 0.17m.

2931. Fragment of a heavy decree (?) relief. On the right, a bearded man is seated facing left upon a simple, high and flat base. Letters, the remains of an inscription, scattered

on the surface. Low on the narrow right side the names
from the second use of the relief in Roman times. Good
post-Parthenon style, around 410 B.C. Bad preservation
of the surface. Unknown provenance. Height 0.48 m., width
0.26 m., depth 0.165 m.

1467. Attic decree relief. The inscription below the figures
commemorates the treaty between Athens and Kerkyra
(375-4 B.C.). Athena is represented on the right, Kerkyra
in the centre, and on the left probably Zeus or the Demos of
Athens. Found in 1876 in the Asklepieion at Athens. It would
probably have been placed somewhere on the Acropolis.
About 370 B.C. Total height 0.95 m., width 0.48 m.

1479. The upper part of a simple decree inscription with
relief. Athena gives her right hand to a bearded man, Kekrops
or the Demos of the Athenians. According to the inscription
the decree is the handing over by the treasurers, of the sacred
moneys of Athena (name of the archon, Euthykles, 398/97
B.C.). Post-Parthenon style with sensitive chiselling of the
marble and harmonious rhythm of poses. Height of the
ancient part 0.40 m., maximum width 0.45 m.

1480. The upper part of a decree stele in relief. The
inscription below is a decree of an alliance of the Athenians
with the inhabitants of Thracian Neapolis (Kavala) under
the archon Elpinos, in 356/5 B.C. In the square relief area
Athena on the left welcomes a small figure (dressed in an
archaistic manner) who wears a polos on her head. She is
the goddess of Neapolis. Mediocre but reverent work of that
period. Provenance unknown. Total height 0.50 m., height
of the relief 0.245 m.

1474. Decree relief. Above, a hole for wedging the cornice.
In the centre of the square the Athena Parthenos, facing right,
holds a small Victory in her right hand. Behind is a horseman, in front the worshipper (at a smaller scale). From the

name of the archon Kallistratos it is dated to 355 / 4 B.C. It is an award of the hereditary « proxenia » to Philiskos, an inhabitant of some city of the Hellespont. The relatively faithful rendering of the Athena Parthenos offers evidence of an early classicistic trend (see the opposite decree relief no. 1467). Found in Athens. Total height 0.92 m., height of the relief 0.19 m., width 0.36 m. (Pl. 41).

1481. The decree relief of Molon. The upper part with the heads of the figures is missing. In low relief on the right, a god on a throne facing left; opposite standing, two female figures (Peloponnesos ? and Athena). Below, the beginning of an inscription. *« Under the archon Molon an alliance of Athenians and Arkadians »* etc. Date 362 / 1 B. C. Unknown provenance. Height (ancient) 0.46 m., width 0.48 m.

1489. Heavy plaque (from the base of a statue ?). Two figures in relief, separated the one from the other by a space between, stand on a small separate base. On the right Dionysos, frontal, with short, sleeved chiton, fawnskin, cloak, and high boots, holds an amphora and a kantharos. On the left a woman with her left hand places incense in a high censer. Inferior work of the Hellenistic period with dependence on older works. Found in 1862 in the Theatre of Dionysos. Height 0.85 m., width 0.95 m., maximum depth 0.10 m.

1460. Simple votive slab. It lacks the right upper part. The representation is in fairly low relief. A young man, seated on a rock and facing right, rests with his left hand on his spear. Opposite, the lower body of a young man wearing a cloak. Below, remains of an inscription of the donor with late archaic lettering. The standing young man who is portrayed lower down is the mortal donor who worships a hero, a holy man of the country (Kephalos ?). About 440 B.C. One of the best votive monuments of the period, charming early classical. Found possibly in Attica. Height 0.495 m., width 0.45 m.

1435. Small votive relief. On the right, opposite a young god, seated on an altar, an attractive woman, frontal (Hebe ?), holds in her lowered right hand an oinochoe. The surface much worn. Below the figures the remains of the inscription of the donor. Excellent plastic rendering. End of the 5th century B.C. or later. Unknown provenance. Height 0.43 m., width 0.39 m.

1403. The left part of a votive relief in the form of a shrine. The Kore, frontal, dressed in chiton and himation, holds a torch in her hand. The left hand rests on the edge of an altar. Behind it, in a hollowed plane, is preserved the right hand of a worshipper. The face of the goddess is damaged. The sculptor probably used the type and the magnitude of the Kore from an important cult statue which would have been erected about 420 B.C. in the most sacred Thesmophorion of Piraeus. Good work, somewhat provincial about 350 B.C. Found in Piraeus. Height 0.87m., width 0.60 m. (Pl. 42 a).

3917. Votive relief in the form of a shrine. In the centre Leto, frontal, with sceptre; on the left Apollo Kitharodos; on the right Artemis holds in her hands two small torches (« Phosphoros »). The first two figures are inspired by Athenian statues of the 4th century : Apollo Patroos, a work of Euphranor, is preserved in the original in the ancient Agora (stoa of Attalos), the Leto is known from copies of the 1st century A.D. in the Theatre of Dionysos. The figure of Artemis echoes some Praxitelean statue. It is uncertain if donors also were on the right edge. It is one of the best of the Attic votive reliefs of the period. The figures shaded from above have a balanced composition and have retained the sacred character of the originals.

11

End of the 4th century B.C. Unknown provenance. Height
0.61 m., width 0.49 m.

1950. Votive relief with simple, horizontal epistyle.
On the left, above three steps a large altar (other opinions
suggest a lyre or a ship). Two men in short chitons ap -
proach the altar, the first carries a goose, the second offers
a phiale; at the back, in low relief, a goddess with two
torches. Further to the right the family of the worshipping donors; in front a deer. Found at Palaiochora on Aegina.
Mediocre work but a unique representation. Height 0.46 m.,
width 0.64 m.

693. Statue of a young girl, headless. In the raised, deep
fold of the highly girded chiton she holds a dove. Noteworthy is the rendering of the fluttering folds. Beginning of the
3rd century B.C. Found with the following objects near the
Ilissos. It was a dedication to the Eileithyiai of Agrai (goddesses of child birth). Height 0.74 m. (Pl. 43).

695. Statue of a girl, with its plinth. Seated on the
ground she holds a dove in her right hand. She wears a
chiton gathered together with crossed bands on the chest
and at the back. Simple, charming work of about 300 B.C.
Found in the same place as the adjacent No. 693. Height
0.40 m., width 0.34 m.

3874. Small relief in the form of a cave. Above can be
seen a bust of Pan, a goat, and an animal. Three Nymphs
in dancing posture advance toward a rustic altar. Behind
them the front of the body of Acheloos. On the left three
worshippers. Simple, inferior style about 350 B.C. Found
in 1940 in Hekale (Attica). Width 0.515 m., height with
the wedge 0.28 m.

1445. Small votive relief, dedicated to the Nymphs.
It has the form of a cave. Above it appear five animals.

The three Nymphs dance toward the left in front of an altar. Behind it, Pan plays his pipe. On the left edge the head of Acheloos. Above the first two Nymphs a large hole for hanging. The Nymphs inspired by known prototypes of the 4th century. Pleasant work from the hand of a marble carver. Found at Eleusis. 4th century B.C. Height 0.28 m., width 0.35 m. (Pl. 48).

1448. Relief in the form of a cave, dedication of Telephanes (according to the inscription). Hermes leads in a dance three Nymphs in front of an altar. Around the wall of the cave appear heads of animals, Pan with his pipe and, below, the head of Acheloos. Rough carving about the middle of the 4th century B.C. From the cave of Parnes (in 1846). Unusual square shape. Height 0.65 m., width 0.94 m.

2011. Small relief in the form of a cave, dedicated to Hermes and the Nymphs (remains of an inscription). Pan appears above with his pipe, animals beside him. In the centre of the cave a charming group of three Nymphs, the first seated. In front of them the nude Hermes, inviting them to the dance. The Triad echoes older classical originals ; the figure of Hermes, however, which moves out from the background shows a developed sense of space. About 340 B.C. Found in 1900 in the cave of Vari (Attica). Height 0.52 m., width 0.37 m.

2012. Relief in the form of a cave (rectangular above). On the left a Nymph is seated facing right ; below is the head of Acheloos. In the centre another Nymph standing, frontal. On the opposite edge a third Nymph seated. Outside near the wall of the cave Pan and, facing right, a young hunter. The faces are missing. About the middle of the 4th century B.C. Found in the cave of Vari in 1900.

According to the inscription, dedicated by Eukleus, son of Lakleus. Height 0.47 m., width 0.68 m.

1447. Relief in the form of a cave. Hermes and the Nymphs, an altar. Around the wall animals and below the head of Acheloos. The handsome shape of the cave and the conventional movements suggest a later period, about 300 B.C. Found in Piraeus (Munychia). Height 0.27 m., width 0.38 m.

1879. Relief in the form of a cave. High above appears the personification of the mountain top. On the right Pan « aposkopeuon » (watching). On the left a seated Satyr with his pipe; on the edge a Hermaic stele. Lower the three Nymphs proceed in dancing steps to the left where, below, there is a basin, an outdoor perirrhanterion. Behind it, traces of a windblown mane of a lionhead water-spout and on the right edge the upper body of a god with a horn. At the side, a goat. One of the best of its kind, it has the special feature that the figures are developed on a plane surface and that the inside of the cave was not represented. First half of the 4th century B.C. Found in the cave of Parnes. Height 0.53 m., width 0.52 m.

3942. Votive relief, with narrow frame. There are portrayed twelve large figures, and four smaller. At the left, seated on a stool, facing right, a matriarchal woman, with a polos on her head. At her side stands a lion. On the·right side other figures, standing : a woman holding a key (priestess) ; the second, frontal, has her head and face covered with a cloth or a skin. In the centre, Dionysos, Pan, a goddess holding torches, and a bearded god with horn, probably Trophonios. On each side of him a snake rises. Farther to the right, above a table full of cakes, appear three young men, facing left, with shields, the Kouretes. The last young figures with caps are the two Dioskouroi. Below them four

small figures, the family of the dedicator. Found at Le-
vadeia about 1935. Unique monument by the hand of a
local artist, important for its religious meaning : the ini-
tiation of the covered figure (male or female) to the myste-
ries. The relief was dedicated to Trophonios, to the triad
of the Kouretes and to the other gods. 3rd century B. C.
or later. Height 0.335 m., width 0.925 m.

1420. Heavy plaque with relief figures. The representation is divided into two parts : on the left standing, a
figure facing left, and nearby a bearded man facing right
opposite a young man. Between them, another young man,
frontal. Post-Parthenon style, with nobility in the faces
and an inner rhythm in the poses. It most probably belonged to a large decree relief. About 430 B.C. Unknown provenance. Height 0.45 m., width 0.40 m.

1421. Relief with simple epistyle, without cornice. In the
centre a male figure (in 3/4 view), wearing a himation. In
front of him are preserved two heads, one of a young man,
and one of a woman, facing him. Behind are three women,
standing, the first two with Argive peplos, the third with
Attic, girded. The central one, frontal, holds a sword in
her lowered hand. On the left edge, low, the upper body
of a nude slave in front of an altar (?). Good composition
and variation in the poses of the figures. The scene uni-
dentified, probably mythical. Found near Tanagra, about
1874. Good work, local, with somewhat rough carving
and with influence of an Attic prototype; about 420 B.C.
Height 0.51 m.

1380. Heavy relief plaque with pediment ; dedication
of *Gorgon(illa)* or *Gorgon(iska)* (the inscription below the
figures). In the centre Leto, frontal, with Argive peplos
and sceptre. On the left Apollo Kitharodos; on the right
Artemis with a deer. She wears a short chiton and a

fawnskin. The face is battered. Beginning of the 4th century B.C. with the use of older prototypes. Found at Pharsala in Thessaly in 1887. Rough work of a local marbleworker. Height 0.81 m., width 0.87 m.

1861. Large heavy relief, more probably sepulchral than votive, with a pediment in relief. On the edges two seated figures, on the right a bearded man, on the left a woman. The woman holds in her left hand a spindle, in her right a ball of wool. The bearded man beside her, frontal, holds a rose and an oar (?). Behind the woman a very small maid servant leans against a chair. Another standing figure, young and beardless, frontal, holds an aryballos in a bag. The last on the right at the edge, a standing woman. The composition balanced but not completely successful. Found outside Thebes in 1896. Even though influenced by Attic originals (especially the seated, bearded man) the theme and style are typically Boeotian, with emphasis on the other-world heroization of the figures. The marble very hard, Thespian. End of the 5th century B. C. Height 1.46 m., width 1.28 m.

1892. Heavy square plaque arranged in front as a shrine in low relief. In the centre Leto. On the left Apollo Kitharodos; on the right Artemis, who holds the long double torch diagonally in front of her body. On the right edge a pilgrim, worshipping. The two figures of gods on the edge influenced by cult statues. Found at Kato Vatheia on Euboea, it would have been a dedication to the shrine of Artemis Amarysia. Rough local work of poros. Middle of the 4th century B. C. Height 0.50 m., width 0.60 m., thickness 0.18 m.

703. Torso of a statue of Asklepios, from the neck to the calves of the legs. His left hand rests on his thigh under the himation, which falls in broad vertical folds from below the chest where it is bunched into a horizontal pleat. The god is supported by his staff under his left armpit. Good free copy (of the middle Hellenistic period) of the cult statue of the god. Found in Athens. Height 1.32 m.

1387. Relief with simple horizontal cornice. Four nude young men, « Asklepiads », in well varied poses. On the left a man wearing a himation; at the edge a young hero in a cloak leans on a staff under his armpit. Surface much worn. Found on Kythnos. It portrays the receiving, by Asklepios, of a local hero. 2nd half of the 4th century B.C. The plastic formation of the figures has an Attic character ; the composition, however, has a provincial originality. Height 0.54 m., width 0.93 m.

RELIEFS FROM THE ASKLEPIEION OF ATHENS

The greater part of the votive reliefs of Room B were found in the excavations of the Archaeological Society on the South Slope of the Acropolis, between the Theatre of Dionysos and the Theatre of Herodes Atticus. Here, in 1877 was discovered the Asklepieion of Athens.

The cult of the god in Athens was begun quite late, in 420 - 419, and on private initiative. Telemachos the Acharnian brought the god of Epidaurus from Zea, the harbour of Piraeus. He established him in the Eleusinion of Athens. Immediately thereafter, however, Sophocles received the god « in his home », most probably in the shrine of the hero doctor Amynos, where Sophocles was a priest. The poet took the name of « Dexion » (the Receiver). About 413 - 412 the building of the Asklepieion would have been ready.

The unmerciful battering of the faces in the reliefs from this excavation results from the survival of the shrine of the doctor-god Asklepios up to the very latest period of antiquity (5th century A.D.) The hands of Christian fanatics destroyed the beautiful classic faces, because the destroyers saw them as the « idols » of the faithless.

A sympathetic aspect of the popular religion of antiquity is revealed in the reliefs of the Asklepieion. Works of humble marble - cutters, they nevertheless have a humanity, without ever being crude. The theme, the narrative, the rhythm of stance and movement, the gestures, the facial expressions, the dress, all will attract the gaze of the visitor and arouse the attention of the archaeologist,

1346. The left part of a relief with epistyle and horizontal cornice. Asklepios standing in front of an altar, resting with his staff under his left armpit. On the left behind him two female figures, possibly his daughters Hygeia and Iaso, the last inspired by figures from the Parthenon frieze. Work of a good sculptor with thoughtful composition. A static line is avoided by varying both the poses and the dress of the women. Beginning of the 4th century B.C. Found in the Asklepieion of Athens. Height 0.48 m., width 0.375 m.

2211. Statue of a nude infant, with plinth. Seated on the ground, facing left, turning his body and raising his head. Good rendering of the moon - shaped face of the small boy, but the body is treated summarily. Found in the Asklepieion of Athens, it would have been dedicated to the god. Height 0.46 m., width of the ancient part 0.48 m.

1436. Right part of a relief with cornice. A small slave deposits on the altar (which is rendered in perspective) a small cake from a tray which he holds in his left hand. In front appears the head of a ram. At the back, standing, a man worshipping. About 340 B.C. Unknown provenance, possibly from the Asklepieion. Height 0.57 m., length of the old part above 0.34 m.

793. Small, simple relief. A snake, coiled, raises its head to the left, the tail antithetic. Excellent plastic rendering. The upper part damaged, the rest of the design uncertain. Unknown provenance. Height 0.65 m., width below 0.29 m.

1341. Small simple slab in relief. Facing Asklepios and his two daughters a working man is standing, wearing a short chiton and cap; behind him the heads of two horses. According to the remains of the inscription he is a wagoner who thanks the god for saving him from some danger. This delightful, lightly chiselled work recalls the lost paintings on wood of the Asklepieion. Early 4th century B.C.; one of the older dedications. Found in the Asklepieion of Athens. Height 0.26 m., width 0.28 m. (P l. 42 b).

1338. Relief with low relief pilasters and a simple epistyle. In the centre a large and imposing Hygeia, standing in front of a high altar, extends her hand in blessing to a worshipper wearing a himation. Behind on the right, Asklepios seated on a stool ; behind his knee a snake. Formerly there was preserved above the altar a cross painted in red colour by some Christian, the same person possibly who shattered the heads of the figures. Good work of the end of the 5th century B.C., one of the older examples from the Asklepieion of Athens. Height 0.545 m., width 0.67 m.

2477. Fragment of a relief plaque, double. A. Above, a light carved moulding. Below, in a low relief the front of a temple with pediment; on the left above it is a cock. In front of the pediment a snake is drawɲ. B. In front of two pilasters on the left the upper body of a woman, on the right a bearded head. In the field a doctor's instruments, in low relief. The figures of this rare work destroyed. Found in the Asklepieion of Athens. Beginning of the 4th century B.C. (?). Height 0.27 m., width 0.30 m.

1333. Large relief with two-fold epistyle and a cornice. On the left the remains of the front body of the seated Asklepios. Large and august, Hygeia stands before him, frontally, leaning with her left hand on the trunk of a leafless tree. A procession of pilgrims advances from the left toward the low altar. A small slave brings a ram. On the right, pilgrims. The last woman on the right holds in her hand above her head a large ciste, with offerings. The work, though a little inferior, has good composition and variation of poses and of planes for the pilgrims. About the middle of the 4th century B.C. Found in the Asklepieion of Athens. Height with the wedge for joining 0.83 m., width of the old part 0.97 m.

1388. Relief of three figures, with simple cornice. In the centre Asklepios, seated on a rock; on the right, standing, his wife Epione or his daugher Hygeia. On the left, an unknown hero. From the Asklepieion of Athens. Beginning of the 4th century B.C. Height 0.60 m.

1339. Relief in the form of a shrine with three figures in low relief. In the centre Asklepios seated on a chair; on the left, Hygeia or Epione ; opposite a pilgrim worshipping. Surface much worn. Beginning of the 4th century B.C. From the Asklepieion of Athens. Height 0.45 m., width 0.68 m.

1373. Small relief. It lacks the upper part of the heads. The two figures facing. On the right Asklepios, on the left a young man nude. Very probably the god held a phiale above the head of the young man. Delicate style about 380 B.C. with influence from older works. Found in the Asklepieion of Athens. Height of the old part 0.41 m., width 0.42 m.

1343. Plaque with one single figure. A young woman standing, looking left, with head bowed, holds in her hands a large horn of plenty. On the epistyle is written : *Agathe Tyche*. About the middle of the 4th century B.C. According to one opinion the figure recalls the statue of the Agathe Tyche of Praxiteles. From the Asklepieion of Athens. Height 0.36 m., width 0.51 m.

1367. The right part of a large relief in the form of a shrine. Shaded by the cornice, four figures of pilgrims in high relief. Further to the left, the lower legs of a nude young Asklepiad, frontal. The heads of the figures are missing.

It would have been one of the better examples of the period. The figures have variation in their poses. In the large open space behind and above them there would have been painted a tree (influence of paintings on wood). From the Asklepieion of Athens. End of the 4th century B.C. Height 0.68 m., width of the ancient part 0.575 m. (with the plaster restoration).

1351. Fragment of relief. An unusual representation of a landscape. Behind a rock rises Apollo ; beside a palm tree, lower on the left, a woman. In the foreground below, a young man clad in a chlamys runs toward a dog climbing a rock. Below, a snake and another dog. The subject is unexplained. Apparent influence of some picture by a painter on wood. 2nd half of the 4th century B.C. From the Asklepieion of Athens. Height 0.85 m., width 0.27-0.28 m.

1352. Left part of a relief. On a rich stool is seated, facing right, Asklepios. Surrounded by three or four of his daughters, he embraces the youngest. Below, a huge snake. In front of him is seated his wife Epione. The identification is confirmed by the « E » which is preserved. Three other names were carved : *Akeso, Iaso, Panakeia*. On the right the lower body of a kneeling (?) boy. Doubtful whether he belongs to the family of the god. Preservation poor. 2nd half of the 4th century B.C. Height 0.53 m., width 0.68 m.

1332. Relief of Athenian doctors in the form of a shrine. On the left, behind Demeter seated on a well (or the « mystic basket ») stands Persephone with two torches. In front of the figures Asklepios standing, receives six worshippers wearing himatia. Below the representation, five large olive wreaths in low relief and the names of five dedicators. One name on the epistyle. They were Athenian doctors, the three sons of famous doctors. The wreaths bear witness to the honour which the city gave to the persons shown here. 2nd half of the 4th century B. C. The connection of Asklepios with the gods of Eleusis is known; the representation, however, is unique. From the Asklepieion of Athens. Height 0.86 m., width 1.15 m. (Pl. 45 a).

1461. The right part of a relief in the form of a shrine. On the left, in front of a tree, the left arm of the seated Demeter. Beside her Persephone, standing, frontal, holds slanting two large torches. On the right, the worshippers. 2nd half of the 4th century B.C. Found in Piraeus. Persephone recalls a cult statue, probably Praxitelean. Height 0.53 m., width 0.37 m.

1369. Right part of a votive relief with epistyle and cornice. In front of an altar (rendered in perspective) are standing Asklepios and Athena, with bodies frontal. The latter leans on the rim of her shield. The figures of the two in their rhythmic monumental pose and the good plastic rendering recall important prototypes. Behind the altar is preserved the body of a small worshipper of Athena. Found in the Asklepieion of Athens. About the middle of the 4th century B.C. Height 0.70 m., width 0.48 m.

1377. Relief in the form of a shrine. On the left, from the same piece of marble, the side view of a tall temple, prostyle with pediment. In front of a fluted column Epione is seated, facing right. Behind her stands Asklepios and, in the background, frontal, one of his daughters. On the right, a couple and eleven faces of worshippers in three planes. On the left a slave with a pig advances. Almost all the faces are battered. On the side faces, low reliefs : on the left, Hekate with polos and with two torches; on the right, a Hermaic stele, bearded. Inferior work, unique in its special form. The smooth surface at the back, unusual in the reliefs of the Asklepieion, suggests the hypothesis that it was prepared for a painted representation which

has perished. About the middle of the 4th century B.C.
Height of the temple 0.65 m., height of the relief 0.49 m.,
width of the whole 0.95 m.

258. The « Asklepios of Munychia ». The upper body
of a large statue of Asklepios. From a separate piece of marble, the left arm together with part of the chest, as well as
the lower body. The head has a marked turning upwards
and to the right; the expression of the face shows suffering
and pathos which are not rhetorical. Eyes of another material inserted. The hair, gathered into high strands above
the forehead, more carefully arranged than the beard. The
anatomy of the chest, carved with amplitude, has a plastic grandeur in the distribution of mass and in the delicate treatment of the skin. The sculptor has given a pathe-
tic expression to the classical type of the god (compare
the spiritual expression of statue no. 265). Without doubt
it would have presented the rhythm of movement with
dramatic revelation. Found in 1888 in Piraeus. Height 1 m.
(P l. 44).

1360. Fragment of a relief. The upper body of Asklepios seated on a throne. He has his head bowed (a band
around his hair) and the hands clasped around his knees,
in reflective meditation. From the Asklepieion of Athens.
Other interpretations suggest a poet or Asklepios in the
act of healing. 2nd half of the 4th century B.C. Height
0.14 m., width 0.20 m.

2557. The right part of a simple votive relief, without
architectural form. In the centre on a square base, a high
stele. Above it, a votive relief. Below and in front of the
stele rises a snake. On the left, the thigh of the seated Asklepios, who is not preserved. On the right, Hygeia standing,
leaning with her left hand on the stele, with the other on
her hip. Her head is missing, the whole surface very worn.

The pose of Hygeia is elegant. About the middle of the
4th century B.C. Found in Athens (Metropolis Square) ;
it would have been a votive to Asklepios. Height 0.71 m.,
width above 0.42 m.

1345. Two parts of a relief with horizontal cornice.
On the left : Asklepios standing in a statue-like pose, standing by his side his wife Epione, the two frontal. On the
other part: a procession of worshippers with two children
in the foreground. On the edge a maid-servant carries on
her head a large basket of offerings. The central part with the
altar is missing. The heads of the figures are preserved.
About the middle of the 4th century B.C. The type of the
Asklepios recalls his cult statue. From the Asklepieion of
Athens. Height 0.49 m., width 0.62 m.

1335. The right part of a votive relief. On the edge,
seated on a throne, Asklepios; behind, Hygeia, slender, leans
against the trunk of a tree which is in the centre of the
composition (around it a snake). In the front in the second plane, a priest and a young acolyte, who holds a tray
with offerings. In the first plane an altar with cakes, by
the side of a man in a himation. On the epistyle, the remains
of the names of the dedicators. The dependence on painted
prototypes is evident in the perspective representation
of the throne, the foot-stool and the altar, as well as in the
rendering of the successive planes. About 330 B.C. Found
in the Asklepieion of Athens. Height 0.58 m., width of the
old part 0.62 m.

1841. Relief, with representation of the « incubation » of
a patient, represented wrapped up on a couch. Standing
above, a god-like figure spreads his hands in a gesture of
healing. Seated in front of the couch on a chair facing right
Asklepios caresses with his left hand the arm of the patient,
and in the other hand holds the sceptre. The first standing

man would be one of the sons of Asklepios, Podaleirios or
Machaon. On the epistyle the inscription : *During the priesthood of Diaphanes, son of Apollonios.* From the Asklepieion
of Athens. End of the 5th century B.C. Height 0.60 m.,
width 0.76 m.

2441. Fragment of a relief with similar representation.
On the right, frontal, Asklepios standing. Around his staff,
a snake. Below, remains of a votive inscription. Most probably from the Asklepieion. Beginning of the 4th century
B.C. Height 0.28 m., width 0.22 m.

2373. The lower part of a votive relief. Preparation for
the « incubation » of the patient. A worshipper and a woman place the patient on a couch. On the right, standing,
Asklepios and Hygeia. Good technique about 410 B.C.
Found near the Kerameikos. Height 0.30 m., width 0.71 m.

1434. Small simple plaque with low relief. A snake rising facing left. Inscription : *Herakleides to the god.* Dedication to Asklepios or to Zeus Meilichios. Found in Piraeus.
Height 0.33 m., width 0.19 m.

3329. Small votive relief with pediment. A large coiled
snake raises its neck high. In front on the left placed high,
a married couple and child. Below an inscription : *Aristomenes to Zeus Meilichios.* First half of the 4th century
B.C. Found in Athens in 1888. Height 0.39 m., width 0.235 m.

1408. Small, simple votive relief. Worthy of note for
its rare theme : a woman kneels in front of a god seated on a throne (Zeus Melichios ?). Behind her follow the
worshippers. First half of the 4th century B.C. Not known
whether it was found in Athens or in Piraeus. Height 0.25 m.,
width 0.40 m.

2565. High votive relief. Along the whole lower part
rises a huge snake. On the flatter part above is attached

a large sandal. Above it, a relief figure of a man standing in worship, facing right. Below the sandal the inscription: *Silon dedicated* (it). The base is missing. A good work, about 360 B.C. The unique representation has been interpreted as the « canting device » (or symbol) of the « Hero in the slipper » (the sandal) whom they worshipped near the Theatre of Dionysos. The relief was found nearby in 1904. Total height 2.39 m., height of the sandal 0.515 m., width below 0.13 m.

1429. The right part of a votive relief in the form of a shrine. Above the central altar, with slanting arrangement, appears the upper body of a young acolyte who holds a cow's head. Eight members of the family follow, worshipping. On the right edge in low relief, a large basket on the head of a maid-servant. The presence of three girls on the right in rhythmic step lends variety to the composition. The heads of the figures are preserved. About 350 B.C. Found in Piraeus, a votive to the Asklepieion there. Height 0.55 m., width 0.51 m.

3304. The central part of a small votive relief with wedge. On the right a man wearing a himation leads a bull toward an altar placed on the left above a square base. On his left arm he holds an infant (in its hand a rattle). Behind, the right hand of another worshipper. First half of the 4th century B.C. Found in the Asklepieion of Piraeus. Total height 0.30 m., length 0.24 m.

1397. Relief with simple epistyle. It lacks the central part. In low relief, on the right of the bed of a partly reclining patient, Amphiaraos, standing in the manner of Asklepios. Behind him, an adolescent young man. End of the 5th or early 4th century B.C. From the Amphiareion at Oropos (in 1890). Height 0.37 m., width 0.50 m.

1384. The right part of a relief. A slave, frontal, holds a tray with offerings; a bearded man stretches his hand toward them. There follow a woman, three children, and the maid-servant with a large basket on her head. Behind the slave, in the second plane, a relief placed on a high base. On the epistyle the names of the dedicators. The faces of the first two have portrait characteristics. From Rhamnous, it would have been an offering to the shrine of Amphiaraos there. Height 0.53 m., width 0.49 m.

2743. The left part of a relief. Worshippers facing right, bearded, with himation, eight in the lower series. Higher behind them appear five persons of whom the first two seem to be women. In front the head of a youth. On the right edge is preserved the hand of a god with a phiale. A little variation from the monotony of the representation in the varying heights of the front figures. The influence of votive paintings on wood is apparent. First half of the 4th century B.C. Found at Nemea. Height 0.33 m., width 0.39m.

1439. Small relief with pediment. The two Dioskouroi, facing one another, leaning on spears, look at a cock-fight below. Simple, pleasant work. Found at Aigeira in Achaia. Local work of the first half of the 4th century B.C. Height 0.40 m., width 0.30 m.

3369. Relief in the form of a shrine, offering of Archinos to Amphiaraos (according to the inscription below the figures). On the left Amphiaraos, standing, is treating the right shoulder of the young man. The latter is represented, again at the back, asleep on the bed, while the snake glides over his shoulder. On the edge a third scene : the dedication of a stele with relief by Archinos to the shrine of the god. High in the centre of the cornice two apotropaic eyes. Found in the precinct of Amphiaraos at Oropos. A splendid example of its kind, noteworthy for its representation of successive episodes. First half of the 4th century B.C. Height 0.49 m., width 0.545 m. (Pl. 47 a).

1395. The left part of a relief with a family of worshippers. On the edge a girl with a large basket on her head. In front an acolyte leads a ram and a pig for sacrifice. First half of the 4th century B.C. Found at the Amphiareion at Oropos (in 1887). Height 0.50 m., width 0.49 m.

3526. Simple relief with figure in fairly high relief. A bearded man wrapped in a himation, slightly bowed toward the left, holds up an enormous leg. The swelling of the veins shows the nature of the illness and the reason for the dedication. Below left, two feet in the middle of a square. According to the inscription, an offering of Lysimachides son of Lysimachos the Acharnian (possibly the one who was Archon in 339/38). Unique of its kind. Found on the west slopes of the Acropolis where there was a shrine of the hero doctor Amynos. End of the 4th century B.C. Height 0.71 m. width 0.34 m. (Pl. 47 b).

1392. Simple relief plaque. On the left is seated on a throne in god-like amplitude, Asklepios, facing right, holding the sceptre in his left hand; below, a footstool. Standing by his side, Epione, frontal. In the centre a hero with short chiton and cloak has his left hand on the head of a horse, while with his right hand he offers to the god an indeterminate object. In front of the horse, a nude young groom. The hero (according to one opinion Hippolytos) has in his pose the rhythm of the 5th century. The relief belongs to the beginning of the 4th century B.C. Found in 1885 at Epidaurus. (Sanctuary of Asklepios). Height with the wedge 0.46 m., width 0.72 m.

1424. Heavy plaque with relief representation. A « divine infant », large, with body frontal, half-seated holding in his hand a dove (?). He has turned his head to the left, toward a young female figure, dressed in a diaphanous chiton. According to one opinion, it is the small Asklepios with his nurse Trygon. The figure, however, (who also holds a bird) seems to be a girl (daughter of Asklepios ?). Found at Epidaurus. Of the 4th century B.C. Local work. Height 0.57 m., width 0.83 m.

265. Statue of Asklepios, bearded, with its plinth and square base. He wears a himation and leans with his left elbow on a staff around which coils a rising snake. The studied contrast of the limbs, the spiritual expression of the face, and the quality of the carving date the work to the beginning of the 4th century B.C. Found at Epidaurus (Sanctuary of Asklepios) in 1886. Total height with base 0.60 m., height with plinth 0.56 m.

1426. Votive relief with simple horizontal cornice. The representation is divided into two parts with the central figures facing one another : two young men standing with hunting dogs which are scenting a trail in front of their feet. They are the sons of Asklepios, Machaon and Podaleirios. On the right Asklepios, frontal, is standing in front of the altar, which worshippers, a husband and wife, approach. On the left edge, opposite one of the Asklepiads, a charming group of three goddesses. The first goddess, seated on a round basket, would be Epione; standing behind her two of the daughters of Asklepios, the right figure holding a hare. Almost all the heads are battered. The somewhat asymmetrical spacing of the composition and the simplicity of the scheme show the influence of painted wooden plaques. 2nd half of the 4th century B.C. Found in 1885 at Epidaurus. Height 0.38 m., width 0.59 m.

1429A. The left half of a relief. Seventeen worshippers in three successive series, one above another ; in the lowest, four youths; in front the back of a figure. By the pilaster on the left the figure of a bearded man in low relief. All the six of the uppermost series bearded. First half of 4th century B.C. Evident influence of votive panels painted on wood. Found in the same place as the next relief no 1402. (See no. 2743). Height 0.40 m., width 0.29 m.

1402. Relief in the form of a shrine. In the centre Asklepios leaning on his staff, facing left. Behind him, standing, his two doctor sons, Podaleirios and Machaon, as well as his three daughters, Iaso, Akeso, and Panakeia. Opposite the god, a family of four worshippers and in the first plane two youths. Behind is drawn the head of a maid-servant. She has a large basket of offerings on her head. At the feet of the god a sacrificial pig. Good Attic work with careful variation of poses. First half of the 4th century B.C. It was kept (before 1821) with others in the monastery at Loukou in Kynouria. The inscription modern. Height 0.53 m., width 0.74 m. (Pl. 45 b).

364. Group of five standing figures. Their heads are missing. In the centre, embracing, a nude boy and a girl who holds a bird. On the right another nude boy; at his right a small girl, shorter, with a long chiton. On the left a short figure wearing a himation (a donor or member of the family of Asklepios, as are the children). The figures are mounted on a single elliptical plinth, the central ones set further back. Found at Epidaurus in 1884. Local craft, inferior, but not unattractive. The back casually worked. 2nd half of the 4th century B.C. Height 0.55 m., width 0.52 m.

FOURTH SMALL ROOM OF VOTIVE RELIEFS

1487. Relief plaque, possibly the front of a throne. The decoration in two successive zones. Below, a lion attacks a deer; above, an oriental with a long chiton, sleeved, a high hat on his head, spreads his hands above the horns of two winged animals who raise, symmetrically, their front legs. Work with the influence of « barbarian textiles » with eastern design. 4th century B.C. Hymettos marble. Found in Athens in 1879. Height 0.93 m., width 0.64 m.

1509. Small simple relief with representation of a « funeral feast ». On the right, on a couch, is a god or hero, half-extended, with polos on his head. In his raised right hand he holds a rhyton. In front, a round tripod table and opposite on the left a woman seated on a stool, with polos on her head. Above, remains of a votive inscription. Found at Argos in 1890. Local work, clumsy carving of the marble. 4th century B.C. Height 0.28 m., width 0.31 m.

3245-3247. Three plaques with figures in low relief of the Eumenides. 3246. The heaviest and best preserved. The three Eumenides step toward the right, with snakes entwined around their arms. Height 0.25 m., width 0.22 m. 3245. They hold snakes and flowers. Opposite them a husband and wife worshipping. Inscription above : « *The woman of Argos* (offers) *prayers to the Eumenides* ». Height 0.41 m., width 0.25 m. Found east of Argos where there was a sacred grove of the Eumenides. They would have been worshipped there as chthonian deities of the fertility of the fields and of women. Known since 1879. Of the 4th century B. C., probably. Typically Argive is the clumsy, sketchy carving.

1914. Relief of three figures, with simple pediment. In the centre seated on a stool Odysseus, with cap on his

head, has one foot in the basin and extends his hand toward his nurse Eurykleia who bows in fright. On the right
Penelope standing in front of a large loom (her body is
viewed from the back) holds a distaff in her hand. Found
at Gonnoi in Thessaly. The carving of the marble is typically Thessalian. Contrast between the matriarchal, heavy
figure of Penelope and the slender form of Eurykleia. Offering to some shrine. The prototype of the relief would
probably have been a painting on wood. The figure of Eurykleia must be dated after 350 B.C., while Penelope recalls an older prototype. Height 0.73 m., width 0.77 m.
(Pl. 46).

1731. Circular altar (?) with low base. The whole upper
and middle parts are missing. Of the twelve gods which
were around it in a somewhat spaced arrangement, eight
gods are preserved. On the left, a goddess facing a god seated on an open - air altar (Poseidon ?). Behind him, Demeter seated facing right, Athena, and farther to the right Zeus seated on a throne facing left. Standing behind
him Hera and Apollo, turned antithetically, seated, holding the kithara. Remains of another figure. Inferior carving, the faces lifeless. Found in 1877 in Athens, north of
the Stoa of Attalos. 1st half of the 4th century B.C. Height
0.44 m., width 1.78 m.

1464. Long base with relief representations on three
sides. On the long, best preserved side, teams of horses and
three grooms, nude. On the narrow side a young horse (a
race horse), facing right. The back panel has d' appeared,
traces of standing figures discernible. Above, a hollow for
the insertion of a votive stele. The other side view was
destroyed in the second use of the base. According to one
view the reliefs were connected with the equestrian victories
of Alkibiades and the stele would have lauded them. Found

in 1861 in Athens east of the Tower of the Winds. Height
0.35 m., width 1.51 m., depth 0.32 m.

3872. « Funeral feast », votive. On the right on a couch
a god is extended, with polos on his head. In his right hand
he raises a rhyton. In front, a table; below it, a dog. On
the left, a woman seated, burning incense. Behind, a small
slave, frontal, and an amphora. Worshippers are not represented. Around the middle of the 4th century B.C. Found
in 1940 at Kalamaki (Phaleron). Height with wedge 0.55
m., width 0.57 m.

1519. Relief in the form of a shrine, the representation
in two parts. On the right a « funeral feast » with a god extended on a couch and a goddess seated beside him. In
front a table with cakes. On the left, behind another similar table sit Demeter and Persephone. On the left edge,
a volute krater with base and standing, a small boy who raises an oinochoe. Underneath, the inscription: *Lysimachides
dedicated* (this to the god). All the figures frontal. Impos-
sible to identify the god and the woman. Found in 1885 in
the sanctuary at Eleusis. End of the 4th century B.C. Height
0.37 m., width 0.71 m.

1422. Heavy relief plaque with narrow frame and cornice, dedicated to the Chthonian gods. On the left Pluto
is seated on a chair. In the centre, Persephone and Demeter frontal, the first with girded peplos and polos, the second with ungirded peplos. On the right, two small girls,
probably mythical priestesses, the first a water carrier,
the second holding a pail. Found at Tegea. Graceless work
of a local marbleworker. The figures hieratic and venerable. Height 0.62 m., width 0.92 m.

2202. Part of a statue of a woman who holds a small boy with her left arm. (There is preserved only a part of her chest). The child clinging to her, frightened, embraces her with his right hand. The plastic rendering of the material is excellent around the lower body of the child. His whole figure has an overwhelming tenderness. The interpretation as Erichthonios whom one of the daughters of Kekrops holds is confirmed by the site where it was found : the south slopes of the Acropolis. It would have been placed above there or in one of the shrines on the slopes. End of the 4th century B.C. Height 0.40 m., width 0.32 m.

262. Statue of the « armed Aphrodite ». She wears a diaphanous chiton which bares the right side of her breast, and also a himation girded. Around her chest is tied the sheath of a sword. In her right hand, slightly raised, she would have held her sword, with the other, lowered, the edge of her himation. She bends her head toward the side of the supporting leg. Deep pleats on the himation; the carving careful, dry. Found in Epidaurus in 1886. Work of a sculptor of Athens, of the first century A.D. The original would have been an important creation, probably of a Peloponnesian sculptor, about 400 B.C., dependent on post-Pheidian sculptures. Height 1.51 m.

175. Statue of the small Ploutos. It belonged to a large statue of Eirene who was holding Ploutos, copy of a (bronze?) work of the first Kephisodotos, placed in the Athenian Agora in 370 B.C. (in the Munich Glyptothek is the more famous copy). Under the body of the child is preserved the arm of the goddess as well as part of the horn of Amaltheia which she held in her hand. Found in the harbour of Piraeus in 1881. It would have been part of the cargo of the same ship as other statues in the Piraeus Museum, also ordered from neo - Attic workshops of the 1st century A.D. The marble of the Ploutos does not seem to be Greek. Height 0.65 m.

189. Head of a young man. It turns toward the left shoulder; the frame is strongly built, almost three - dimensional; the expression has power, with the projecting chin; the gaze is hard and vacant. A good copy of the 1st century A.D. of a type known from a famous statue called the « Ares Ludovisi ». According to one opinion the head would have belonged to a sepulchral statue (heroization of the deceased ?). Found in 1867 in Athens (Stoa of Eumenes). Height 0.32 m.

1623. Torso of the statue of a nude youth. The statue was a copy of the Apollo Sauroktonos of Praxiteles and had retained from the prototype the transposition of the body weight to the tree which supported it. Work of the Roman period. Unknown provenance. Height 0.70 m.

1463. Triangular base of a bronze tripod. It had, on three sides, figures in high relief which stand on a horizontal strip.
A. Dionysos, facing left, dressed in the sleeved chiton of the theatre and with a himation, holds a thyrsos and a kantharos. B. Winged Nike, facing left, with phiale. Inspired by a figure of the east frieze of the Parthenon. C. A similar figure with oinochoe in the hand, confronting the god. The upper section missing, battered. Work of the middle of the 4th century B.C. with influence of Praxitelean creations in A. and C. Found in 1853 in Athens (street of the Tripods). Height 1.30 m., width 0.70 m. (Pl. 51).

1777. Head of the Apollo Kitharodos, with the neck. It was inserted in a large statue. The neck framed by locks of hair. Serious expression, vacant gaze. Good work of the 4th century B.C. influenced by an important contemporary creation. Back unworked. Unknown provenance. Height 0.40 m.

240. The « Hermes of Atalante ». Statue of a young man, nude, with its plinth. The cloak, thrown over his shoulder and left arm, falls on the cylindrical support. He stands upright on both feet, the right leg relaxed. In his left hand he would have held his staff. It was probably a grave statue of a young man in the form of Hermes, though the facial characteristics are not those of a portrait. Found at Atalante. Mediocre work of the 2nd century A.D., more probably an eclectic composition than a copy of a classical original. Height 1.90 m.

194. Small head of a young man, rather flat, square. The marked turning toward the left, the hollowed eyes, the expression of anguish with the half open mouth suggest an origin from the pediment of some temple. Unknown provenance. Height 0.17 m.

3989. Small statue of Demeter. Seated on the mystic basket, she holds in her left hand ears of wheat and poppies. Probably of the 2nd century A.D., copy of a good classical original. Found in the Ancient Agora of Athens in 1907. Total height 0.39 m., depth of the statue below 0.37 m.

1733. The « base of Bryaxis ». A square base of a votive tripod, with reliefs on three sides : a horseman advances toward a tripod. On the undecorated side a fine inscription with the names of three victorious phylarchs and (below in small letters) the signature of the sculptor : *Bryaxis made* (me). Found in 1891 north east of the Theseion. The reliefs, somewhat conventional, would have been carved about the middle of the 4th century B.C. before the Karian sculptor was engaged in work on the Mausoleum. The surfaee is blackened from storing the base during the war years. Width 0.74 - 0.75 m.

183. Large head of a statue of the type of the « Lykeion Apollo » (for the pose see the adjacent small statue no. 1812). Found in 1888 on the seashore at Laurion in the slag from the mines (which had blackened its surface). A faithful, crude copy of Roman times. Height 0.32 m.

1812. Small statue of Apollo, nude, with the right arm above his head in a relaxed pose. A delicate Hellenistic work, copy of an important creation of the 4th century, the so - called Lykeion Apollo. Found in Epidaurus in 1887. Height 0.32 m.

184. Head of Apollo from a statue related to no. 1812 (the type of the body is not known). The head, which inclines toward the left shoulder, and which has a slight upward look is supported principally on the left hand above which the right falls gently. Generous use of the drill in the hair. Back surface unworked. A good copy of the beginning of the 2nd century A. D. of an inspired creation of the 4th century, possibly Skopaic. Found in Athens in 1875. Height 0.38 m.

Br. 13396. The « youth from Antikythera ». Large bronze statue of a young man, nude, a god or hero rather than an athlete. The weight of the body falls on the left leg, while the right is drawn back. In deliberate contrast the left arm hangs freely and the right, extended, is raised. In spite of all attempts it remains doubtful what he would have held in his open fingers. It is not credible that he represented Perseus lifting the head of Medusa. The interpretation as Paris with the apple is more plausible. The rhythm of the pose, balanced, harmonious, and the muscular emphasis of the pelvis come from the tradition of the Polykleitan canon. Later details are the delicacy of the slender legs, the slight proportions of the parts of the body, the expression of the face with inset eyes (one restored). A courageous « musical » work of a sculptor of the North Peloponnese about 340 B.C. probably by the Sikyonian Euphranor. Found in pieces on the ocean bed off Antikythera in December 1900. It was immediately assembled and boldly restored, especially the chest. In 1951-52, after some months of effort, a new assembly and restoration were produced in the work rooms of the National Museum under the Director, Christos Karouzos, by the sculptor Andreas Panagiotakis and the chief technician John Bakoulis through a donation from I. Lagonikos. Total height 1.94 m. (Pl. 52).

Br. 15187. Bronze head of a woman with thick neck, from a large statue. A slight inclination toward the left shoulder. The hair, drawn up high, leaves the ears free and the head is bound round with a plait, raised above the high forehead; meditative gaze, vague. A cluster of wavy locks rises above the ears, toward the plait, exactly as in a similar bronze head from Herculaneum. Both are considered copies of the Roman period of a statue of the 4th century which represents a poetess (Sappho ?). Found on the site of Thracian Perinthos. The thinness of the bronze shows an advanced technique in bronze casting. The head was cast separately from the statue. Gift of I. Stamoulis. Height 0.34 m.

1762. Large head of Aphrodite with a long neck. It has a slight turn toward the left; a flat band around a flat hairdress which ends behind in a chignon (the edge of this from another piece of marble). In early Christian times, above the triangular forehead, was carved a cross, another smaller on the chin, to expiate the ancient goddess. Found in Athens in 1889 near the Tower of the Winds. The statue, a remarkable work of the 2nd century A.D., was a copy of an important Praxitelean original. Formerly it showed traces of colour. Height 0.45 m., length 0.35 - 0.32 m.

2133. Head of Aphrodite, crude copy of the Knidia of Praxiteles. The back part is missing. Double band around the hair. Found in Athens. Height 0.28 m.

192. Head of a woman, with slender neck (formerly inserted in a statue). It has a slight turning toward the left, the hair is bound above. Holes in the ears for metal ear-rings. A good but spiritless copy of the 1st century A.D. of an elegant original (the end of the 4th century B.C.)

4019. Statue of Artemis, the lower body missing. She wears a chiton and peplos with foldover. She moves forward, turning her head to the right and advancing the left leg. High on her back is her quiver. Her face has portrait characteristics; this would have been a grave statue of a girl who was portrayed as belonging to the retinue of the goddess. For the prototype see the head no. 550. Found in 1950 or 1951 near Pentalophos in Aitolia. Height 0.52 m.

550. Head of Artemis. She has turned toward the right, a band around her head. Her hair covered her neck. The whole statue was a provincial copy of the Roman period of an original (known from the better copy as the « Artemis Colonna »), a work probably of the North Peloponnesian school, of the end of the 4th century B.C. Found in Thebes in 1883. Height 0.27 m.

1656. Statue of Dionysos « Sardanapalos » (the name from another copy in the Vatican, inscribed). He has a long beard and is dressed in chiton and a himation which, hieratically imposing, doubled over his chest, covers his whole body. The arms and lower body are missing. Found in 1865 near the Theatre of Dionysos. Copy of the 1st century

A.D. of a bronze original, probably Attic, post - Praxitelean.
See the adjacent head no. 3478. Height 1.97 m.

3478. Large head of Dionysos in excellent condition,
Above the low forehead fall the locks of hair, in spirals
in front of the ears. Long beard with accurate delineation.
The face smooth. One of the cold, accurate works of the
classicism of the 1st century A.D. For the type see the
adjacent statue no. 1656. Found in Piraeus in 1914. Height
0.34 m., depth 0.28 m.

354. Bust of a woman, once inserted in a statue. The
hair gathered together on the head is arranged in strips
(«Melon » style). The back is missing. In that position the himation or a veil would have covered the head. Slight turning
toward the left. Good, cold replica of the 1st century A.D.
of a known original of the 4th century B.C. Unknown provenance. Height 0.33 m.

3412. Statue of Eros, modest copy of the bronze Eros from
Thespiae, creation of Lysippus (about 330 B.C.). Found in
his native town, Sikyon. Work probably of the 1st century
B.C. Height 0.33 m.

178-180. Three heads from the pediment of the temple
of Athena Alea at Tegea. (It was built after 395 B.C. when
the old temple burnt down). On the eastern pediment was
represented the hunt of the Calydonian boar, on the western
the struggle of Tegean Telephos with Achilles in the river
Kaikos near Troy. The architect and sculptor was the Parian
Skopas.

178. Head of the boar from the eastern pediment. The
lifelike eyes have a pathos almost human. Holes for attachment. Height 0.30 m., width 0.40 m.

179-180. Head of a beardless man and head of a warrior with Attic helmet. The first (height 0.22 m.) turns
sharply toward the left shoulder, the other is turned upward.

Known since 1878, in the National Museum since 1885, they were the first to reveal the powerful pathos of Skopaic art : the muscular modelling emphasized, the inner fire, the cubic formation, the small face, the eyelids swollen above the prominence of the eye sockets — all preludes of the Hellenistic style. In the small Museum of Tegea are all the remaining sculptures of the temple, which were found in subsequent excavations.

In the inside of the same temple of Tegea would have been placed the cult statue of the goddess Hygeia the famous head of which is preserved.

3602. In the rendering of the ideal figure this work reaches the peak of Classical Greek art. The serene beauty of a woman has been raised to aethereal divinity. The hair drawn back from the forehead in a simple linear style, leaving her small ears uncovered, is gathered into a knot behind. The inclination of the head to the left gives her a tenderness and a pensive look and would have been noticeable in the statue as a whole. Only a great sculptor — who else but Skopas ? — could have conceived and carved both the vivid figures of the pediments and this image which even today gladdens the hearts of mankind. About 360 B.C. It was stolen from the Tegea Museum in 1916 and buried nearby. Found again in 1925 and placed in the National Museum. Height 0.285 m. (Pl. 54).

3004. Large head of Athena with a large raised Corinthian helmet (head of a ram in relief on each panel). Good, far from arid, replica of the Hellenistic period of a serious classical original (about 400 B.C.) The type is known from a better copy as the « Athena Giustiniani ». Found in 1899 in the stoa of Attalos. Height 0.40 m. (Pl. 55).

1810. Statue of the goddess Hygeia with its plinth (triangular behind). Above her back crawls the snake; starting from her left shoulder it coils itself around her right arm. In her lowered left hand she holds the pyxis with the medicines. She turns her head toward the right with a benign expression. Found in 1897 at Epidaurus. A work probably of the 2nd century A.D., it copies a pleasant work of the 4th century placed on the Acropolis. Known from a more complete copy as the type of the « Hygeia Hope ». Height 0.67 m. See the adjacent head no. 186.

186. Head of a statue of Hygeia. It lacks the upper part which was from another piece of marble. A flat band surrounds her hair and is knotted behind. The head is inclined to the left; the glance is somewhat fiery. Use of the drill on the hair. Crude, somewhat free copy of the 2nd century A.D. of a tender classical original, known from many copies. Found in 1878 in the Asklepieion of Athens. (See the preceding statue no. 1810). Height 0.30 m., width 0.28 m.

By the wall:

317-318. Two heads of epheboi, encircled with bands. They are full face, a proof that they come from Hermaic stelai, which would have been set up in order to honour victors in local games. They were found at Rhamnous in 1890. For the type of such Hermaic stelai see no. 313 in the next room. Height 317 : 0.20 m.; 318: 0.22 - 0.23 m.

182. Head of a goddess. It has a slight inclination toward the left shoulder, while it apparently leans on the right hand. The mouth half open, the eyes deep, with their gaze directed upwards. The skilled finishing of the surface (with wax - polish) is evidence of the hand of an important sculptor, perhaps Skopas. From the site where it was found (the Theatre of Dionysos in 1876) and from the Dionysiac « mitra » which encircles the head the whole statue has been interpreted as Ariadne who rests in extended pose. 2nd half of the 4th century B.C. A good copy of the head, a work

13

of the Roman period, is in the Museum of Berlin. Height
0.38 m. (Pl. 53).

323. Bust of Asklepios, bearded, formerly inserted in a
statue. Height 0.36 m.

324. Head of Hygeia (it lacks the upper right part).
The eyes deep, the mouth narrow, very graceful. Height
0.25 m. Good products of the 4th century B.C., both echo
unknown works of an important artist. Found in 1887 on
Amorgos.

231. Large statue of the goddess Themis. She probably held scales in her left hand, in the other a phiale for libation. The high girding as well as the marked accent on the relaxed leg are characteristics of the post-classical period, the 3rd century B.C.; so too is the emphasis on the manner in which the himation is held below her breast. The head inserted. Found in 1890 at Rhamnous in Attica in the temple of the goddess. A good, somewhat provincial work of the sculptor Chairestratos. The name is carved on the square base. In this inscription the statue is identified as a votive of Megakles of Rhamnous. Height 2.22 m. (P l. 56).

245. Statue of Dionysos and Satyr, unfinished. The god, nude, raises his right hand above his bowed head, while with the other he embraces a nude Satyr. The right leg of the Satyr is faintly sketched diagonally on the background; a marked turning inward of Dionysos. The base unworked. Found in Athens outside the precinct of the Olympeion in 1888. Influenced by some larger original, possibly Praxitelean, it would have belonged probably to the end of the classical period (end of the 4th century ?). Height of the figures 0.74 m., and 0.66 m., width of the base below 0.39 m.

215-217. Three plaques of relief figures, three on each one. A. The musical contest of Apollo with Marsyas. The god seated on a rock facing right, clothed in the official dress of the kithara player, holds a large kithara awaiting the issue, motionless, Olympian. On the opposite edge Silenos (Marsyas), in a final effort, plays nervously on his double flute. In the centre, at some distance from the god, a Scythian, upright, full face, stands obediently silent, holding in his hand a knife, ready to flay the already defeated Marsyas. Of the six Muses in the other two plaques five hold musical instruments and scrolls, one is wrapped in her himation. The most graceful of all is the standing figure of plaque no. 216 who holds a double flute. All seem to be inspired by statues. Only in the scene of the punishment of Silenos is the effect of a dramatic narrative rendered successfully. The representation of the Muses is conventional, without imagination, although they have delicate bodies and in their faces a suffusion of a Praxitelean tenderness. Use of the drill in the grooving of perpendicular folds in the garments of the Muses. Together with a fourth plaque which is lost they formed the decoration of the base of a group of three statues. Leto and her two children were represented and were according to Pausanias (VIII,9,1) works of Praxiteles. The hand of some pupil of his would have sketched and executed the reliefs of the base about 320 B.C. Found at Mantinea in 1887. Height 0.98 m., width of 216-217 : 1.365 m., of 215 : 1.385 m.

4553. Statue of a man wearing a himation, headless. He was supported on his staff, under his left armpit, his right hand on his hip which protrudes strongly, counterbalancing the relaxed left leg. Work probably of the 3rd century B.C., it has good carving and a sense of the organic rhythm of the body. Unknown provenance. Height 0.93 m.

181. Bust of « Eubouleus » or of some other Eleusinian « demon » of the lower world. The face, with an inclination toward the right, is framed by the hair, deeply grooved, in disorder, covering his neck. A band around his head. The chiton smooth, the face with pleasing carving and rendering of the skin. The perpendicular cutting of the right shoulder suggests a second use of the work. The use of the drill for the hair, which increased after the 4th century, was demanded by the necessity of rendering chthonic characteristics. Against the recent interpretation of the work as Alexander the Great the two adjacent copies (nos. 1839 and 2650) provide an objection, because they have none of the characteristics of heads of Alexander. Traces of wax-polish are apparent on the face. From the hand of a post-Praxitelean sculptor about 300 B.C. or a little later. Found at Eleusis (in the Ploutonion) in 1885. Height 0.47 m. (Pl. 59).

1839. Head of « Eubouleus ». Copy of the adjacent classical work no. 181. The eyes of another material were inset. A fresh work of the late Hellenistic period, with carefully considered chiselling of the face. Found at Eleusis, near the Telesterion in 1883. Height 0.35 m.

2650. Head of « Eubouleus ». Copy of the adjacent classical work no. 181. Found in Athens. Laboured work of the 1st century A.D. Height 0.34 m.

239. Statue of a young Satyr, « aposkopeuon » (on watch), with its base in the form of a rock. From the left arm hangs a panther skin. Stepping on the tips of his toes, he puts his hand in front of his face, while he looks into the distance. It was probably an acroterion for the pediment of some unknown temple, possibly of Dionysos. Charming work of the early Hellenistic period (the 3rd century B.C.). Found at Lamia, about 1830. Height 0.90 m. (Pl. 60).

224. Small statue of a woman with its round plinth and square base. She wears peplos and himation. The head looks into the distance and toward the left, the same side as the free leg. The hair short. The perpendicular direction of the central fold of the himation from the chest is continued with the folds of the peplos below. The right hand rests on the hip. Found in 1889 at Kissamo in western Crete. A delicate work of about 200 B.C. Height of the figure 0.335 m., with the base 0.365 m.

220. A group of two figures (in the round) with a rectangular plinth. The heads are missing. The first, seated on a rock, facing right, wears a himation and the upper body seems to be nude (for this reason probably male). Behind, a woman standing facing right, slender, in a chiton, himation, and slippers, with her legs crossed. She leans on the shoulder of the other with her left arm. The surface is weathered. Found in 1873 in the Kerameikos but it is unlikely to have been a grave monument. Possibly it was brought there at some time from the Asklepieion (in that case they would be Hygeia and the young Asklepios ?). Careful carving especially in the folds. The composition shows an attempt at variety in the representation of the side view of the two figures. 2nd half of the 4th century B.C. Height of the standing figure 0.85 m., of the seated one 0.67 m., length of the plinth 0.74 m., height 0.07 m.

1226. Grave stele of a young athlete, with simple horizontal cornice. He is nude, full face, and seems to be anointing himself with oil. On the left a small servant holds the strigil. On the right, in a perspective representation, the Hermaic grave stele with the bust of the deceased; below, a large hydria. Bare surfaces above and below the hollowed relief; above would have been painted bands. On the lower part, traces of a carved inscription. It is uncertain whether it was found at Hermione. 2nd half of the 3rd century B.C. at the earliest. Height 0.98 m., width below 0.36 m.

247. Statue of a Galatian, nude, half - fallen, on the defensive. Marked inclination of the body toward the left and forward. The right leg drawn back, bent; the other extended with bent knee. Below by the side of the right leg and joined with it a Galatian helmet is used as a support for the statue. On the part of the chest which is missing the shield would have been fitted in diagonally. Large bare space between the legs.

The plinth of the statue rectangular with an irregular upper surface. The emphasis on depth together with the drawing back of the leg would support a date at the end of the 3rd century B.C. According to other opinions it is a Pergamene dedication or a post-Pergamene work of the 2nd half of the 2nd century B.C. It has still a genuinely ardent pathos in its entire pose and in its anatomic formation, and there are evident traces of the «ganosis» (wax-polish) of the torso. Found in 1883 on Delos. The old association with the inscribed base in the Museum there is doubtful. Height 0.93 m.; width of the base 1.43 m., height 0.05 - 0.06 m.; width of the spread of the legs c. 0.95 m.

366. Head of Alexander the Great, covered with the lionskin of Herakles. It has an inclination to the left. The glance, deep, upward, the half open mouth, give an expression of uneasiness, dominated by pathos. Certain letters carved on the cheeks and on the lionskin are unexplained. Good work, the lionskin has skillful rendering. Probably beginning of third century B.C. Found in the Kerameikos in 1875. Height 0.28 m.

2222. Statue of Aphrodite, headless. The goddess supported by her left elbow on a pillar, is dressed in a chiton, girded high. The himation is wrapped around her waist, the fold reaching as far as her left knee, while the edge of the material, richly pleated, falls in front of the pillar. Her left leg is crossed in front of the other. The plinth is delicate. Charming work, well carved, probably of the 3rd century B.C. Found at Chaironeia. Transferred to the Museum in 1880. Height 0.42 m.

313. Hermaic stele (Herm)˙of a young man, from Rhamnous. The chiton under the himation covers the arms also (the left resting on his thigh). Below the chiton is preserved a small part of the stele. According to the inscription on the round base it was a dedication by the heads of gymnasia after a victory in the contests of the torch races. The back panel is flat. Neat Attic work of the 3rd century B.C. Only recently has the head been given its correct inclination. Height of the statue 0.70 m., height of the base 0.28 m., diameter 0.44 m.

196. Small head of a young man from a Hermaic stele. Delicate face, with noble characteristics. Wreath around the head. Of the 3rd century B.C. Found at Pharsala in Thessaly in 1887. Height 0.115 m.

Sculptures from the cult statues in the temple of the great goddesses in Arkadian Lykosoura. They are all works of the Messenian sculptor Damophon, known especially for his construction of acrolithic statues. To him also was entrusted the repair of the chryselephantine statue of Zeus by Pheidias at Olympia. It is not known exactly whether he lived in the first or in the second half of the second century B.C. According to the description by Pausanias and the evidence of a coin of Lykosoura the two seated statues of the great goddesses, Despoina and Demeter, were in the centre. Standing beside them stood the Titan Anytos and Artemis. The head of Despoina is not preserved. The colossal bodies and other sculptures from the group of statues have stood, since the excavation of 1889, in the local Museum there.

1734. Colossal head of Demeter. High diadem around her hair. By the side and behind the right part of the head falls a lightly folded veil. The pupils of the eyes slightly carved, the mouth small, the hair somewhat disorderly, sketchy, with sparse locks, the face full and round. The surface is not well preserved. The figure retains a certain grandeur. The broad, wind blown surfaces are carved by a worthy hand. (Pl. 57).

1736. Colossal head of the giant Anytos, once inserted

in the standing statue. The hair, swept up from the face, falls at the sides in disorder, restless, as also the beard. The eyes, once inserted, are missing. The expression somewhat vacant, the whole influenced by older classical creations of great sculptors. Height 0.74 m.

1735. Head of Artemis, from the standing statue. It has an inclination toward the left. A diadem around the hair. The eyes, once inserted, are missing. Holes in the ears for ear-rings, and on the temples for the fixing of a metal fillet. The expression of the round, plump face is vacant. It lacks the upper part of the head. Height 0.48 m. The second large statue, Despoina, seated, held against her breast the mystic basket. A relief decorated the footstool and the base: in this also, an echo of Pheidian statues.

2171, 2172, 2174, 2175. Tritons, male and female, from the throne of the goddesses at Lykosoura. No. 2171, the best preserved, has the mystic basket above her head. Behind, her scaly body terminates in a double tail turned toward the centre. No 2174 seems to be female, turning, like no. 2171, forward, while the square body (headless), no. 2172, turns toward the back. All three small statues are delightful, with Hellenistic litheness and grace, the first two also with faces expressive of tenderness. The female Triton, no. 2175, inferior (see especially the scales), cold and unexpressive, may be a replacement in the first century A.D. of an older one of the Hellenistic period. Height, 2171 : 0.50 m., 2172 : 0.28 m., 2174 : 0.42 m., 2175 : 0.51 m. (Pl. 58).

1737. Part of the « sacred fabric » of the goddesses of Lykosoura. Rich relief decoration. On the upper part of the fabric whose decoration is in clear high relief, doubled, a narrow zone with eagles and thunderbolts, another with ornaments. In the centre, another, wider, with Tritons, Nereids, and dolphins. Below, tassels. Lower, on the princi -

pal panel, a broad zone with a Victory facing right, who lifts in front of her a censer. Similar back view. A branch of myrtle or olive in front, perpendicular. In the lower zone dwarfs with animal heads, demons of the Arkadian woods, who run in a dance. Above them, horizontal branches of laurel or myrtle, in the lowest zone running spirals. The narrow right side unworked. A skillful transfer into marble of a rich, folded textile. Found at Lykosoura with the adjacent sculptures in 1889. Total height 1.13 m.

3044. Statue of a young man, nude, headless, of a type similar to the Satyr of Lamia, no. 239, simplified and with one variation : instead of the animal skin a long cloak extends from his left shoulder to the ground; in the back view it has a diagonal trend. Zephyr (?). Found in Athens. End of the 2nd or beginning of the 1st century B.C. Height 0.66 m.

327. Portrait head of Demosthenes, probably from a bust. It was a copy of the head of a bronze creation of the sculptor Polyeuktos which had been set up in the Agora of Athens in 288 B.C. He was represented standing, wearing a himation, slender, with his hands clasped low, his head bowed in silent despair. Good copy of the 2nd century A.D. with an attempt at rendering his personal features, even the defective articulation of the mouth. Use of the drill for the hair. Found in the National Gardens in Athens in 1849. Height 0.28 m. The left cheek and the nose restored.

234. Bust of Athena, once inserted in a statue. It lacks the helmet formerly placed on her head. Her face, rigid and unturning, the lips full, the eyes large. Replica of the type of the Athena of Velletri, not coldly classicistic but with some traces of grandeur and of the Hellenistic pulsation of life. Found with no. 233 in 1837 near the Kerameikos. They would probably have been part of a group of statues, work of the Athenian sculptor Euboulides II. According to Pausanias they represented Athena Paionia, Zeus, Mnemosyne, and the Muses. About 130 B.C. Height 0.60 m.

233. The upper part of a large female statue, probably Victory (holes on the back for the attachment of the wings). She wears a peplos girded high and has a strong antithetic movement, the breast to the right, the lower body and the head to the left. Together with her long neck which contributes an effect of slenderness to the heavy body, the head was inserted in the statue. The expression of the face with the half open mouth lends a somewhat psychic quality; the folds are full of life, windblown — all these indications that the tradition of sculpting had not yet withered, nor the sense of movement, even though, in comparison with the Pergamene works, a seriousness restrains the Attic works from any exuberant outbreak. About 130 B.C., probably a work of the Athenian sculptor Euboulides II. Found in 1837 in the Kerameikos, as was also no. 234. Height 1.22 - 1.23 m., maximum width 0.64 m.

V. 19567. The front section of the head of a young woman, facing right, of Egyptian basalt. Above the narrow triangular forehead the hairdress terminates with the head of a ram, which extended as far as the left ear. The light band of the hair ends in a tail. The queen of Egypt, Arsinoe the second, is represented. A work, probably Attic, of the first half of the 3rd century B.C. Height 0.85 m., maximum width 0.07 m.

4508. Statue of a man wearing a himation, headless. His weight is on the right leg, with his left arm he holds the edge of the himation, which is arranged below in rich, thick folds. From the soft flesh of his arm, one concludes that he represents a philosopher. Excellent work, rare, original, of the 3rd century B.C., probably Attic. Unknown provenance. Height 1.22 m.

4537. Part of a small grave stele of a philosopher or poet. He is portrayed wearing a himation, full face, holding a scroll in his lowered left hand. With its skilled carving and the emphasis on anatomy, it shows in its conventional theme a trace of Hellenistic vitality. This small work gives an impression of the appearance of Hellenistic portrait statues. End of the 2nd century B.C. Found on Anaphe. Height 0.65 m., width 0.19 - 20 m.

3266. Portrait head of a beardless man. It belonged to a statue, probably seated, of some poet of the Attic New Comedy. Found in the stoa of Attalos in 1886. Excellent, rare, original work of the ripe Hellenistic period, about 150 B.C. There is no copy preserved. Height 0.195 m., width 0.25 m.

2811. Part of a small, simple votive relief. A poet, bearded, wrapped in a himation is seated on a heavy official throne, facing left, reflectively holding his right hand to his chin. At the back, in low relief, is sketched the stage curtain of the theatre. Found in 1889 on the west slopes of the Acropolis. Probably of the 4th century B.C. Height 0.21 m., width above 0.16 m., below 0.085 m. (Pl. 64).

On the walls to the left and right of the door theatrical masks of marble. On the left a tragic mask of an old man.

The last two on the right, among the most remarkable of the ripe Hellenistic period (3rd or 2nd century B.C.), are « tragic » and represent types of the New Comedy. Only the upper part is preserved. Unknown provenance.

380. Grave statue of a woman, unfinished. She is portrayed seated on a rock, facing left. She wears a chiton, girded high, and a himation. With the antithetic turning of the left shoulder toward the right the figure leads the eye into the back ground, thus creating an effect of space. The arms are missing, the head inserted. Found on Rheneia, before 1830. Height 1.48 - 1.50 m., length of the rock at the back 0.57 m., height 0.67 - 0.68 m. (Pl. 65).

3373. Heavy comic mask of the « head servant », a known type of the Attic New Comedy. Exaggerated portrayal of the comic features: the snakelike winding of the eyebrows, the asymmetry of the face, the flat snub nose, the turning to the left. The back surface unworked, holes for the attachment of the whole to some building. Found in 1915 near the Dipylon, it was probably placed in the house of the « craftsmen of Dionysos ». Of the 2nd century B.C. Height 0.31 - 0.32 m.

Br. 6439. Bronze head from a portrait statue of a boxer, victor in the games. It has a slight inclination toward the left shoulder. From the wreath of olive around the head two small leaves are preserved. The hair falls richly, spreading all around as far as the neck, leaving exposed the misshapen ears. The forehead slightly wrinkled, a snub nose, the eyes inserted, the carved eyebrows lowered toward the nose. The locks of hair and the beard, curled, have been carved with care. The sturdy structure of the face has unity, without disturbance of the surface. The expression, in spite of the coarse features of the professional athlete, has calm and spiritual depth. Found in 1880 at Olympia. It is considered that this wonderful statue represents the pugilist Satyros and that it was the work of the Athenian sculptor Silanion, one of the Platonic circle. About the middle of the 4th century. It is one of the very few portrait originals in bronze of the classical period. Height 0.28 m.

Br. 13400. The « philosopher of Antikythera ». Bronze portrait head of a bearded elderly man, with part of the front of the neck. Once inserted in a statue. The preservation of the eyes enlivens the expression which is open in observation, full of intelligence. The moustache and generous beard were rendered after the casting, by engraving; the hair falls in clusters of untidy locks, almost uncombed, covering the back of the neck. The lower lip thin, sarcastic, the forehead wrinkled. It portrayed probably a philosopher of northeast racial origin, Bion of Borysthenes. A Cynic, among other things, he established himself in Athens at the end of the 4th century and became famous in all the ancient world for his satiric diatribes. The head, one of the most important and most representative of the psychological studies by an artist of that time, is dated to the 2nd half of the 3rd century B.C. The philosopher was represented standing; to him perhaps belonged the feet with sandals (by the wall; the weight on both soles), an arm and part of a himation. Found in 1901 - 1902 on the ocean bed off Antikythera. The statue possibly stood in the Agora of Athens. Height 0.29 m. (Pl. 61).

1028. Grave stele of the Thasian Nike, rectangular, with a palmette which sprouts from an acanthus. Relief moulding below the epistyle. Above the figures two rosettes. On the left seated on a stool facing right, Nike (her face damaged) « welcomes » a beardless man, standing opposite her. In the centre of the background a small servant girl holds a fan. The name carved below the figures. One of the best island grave stelai of the 2nd century B.C.

Skillful treatment of folds. Found on Tenos at the beginning of the last century. Height of the ancient part 1.54 m. (Pl. 62).

2391. Part of a small grave stele. On the right a woman seated diagonally on a throne facing left, with her head supported on her left hand, looks toward a man standing in front of her. Both have portrait features. In a second plane, high up above a wall, are raised the upper bodies of two children; a third figure is outside the wall. Of the 2nd century B. C. In the inventory is written « Athens », but it is more probable that it was found on one of the Cyclades or in Asia Minor. Height 0.36 m.

1239. Grave stele of Agelais. She is seated on a stool facing left with legs crossed ; the folds richly accented. Her face has portrait characteristics. Opposite her, standing, a small servant girl. The relief is framed by two columns fluted only on the upper part. The pediment restored with plaster. Found possibly on Syros, more probably on Rheneia in 1830. End of the 2nd century B.C. Height of the old part 0.60 m.

4539. Part of a small grave stele of an adolescent youth. There is preserved only a pilaster on the right. He is portrayed standing with the weight on the left leg. The himation leaves his chest bare. He holds a bird in his left hand. The head and feet are missing. Ionian work of the advanced Hellenistic period. Second half of the 2nd century B.C. Found on Anaphe. Height 0.74 m., length 0.48 m.

2772. Small statue of a nude boy, with the plinth. Supported by a small column, with his legs crossed, he presses down on a goose with one hand. A sweet smile suffuses the boy's face. Found at the source of the Kephisos, under the north slopes of Parnassos and near the ancient Lilaia (Polydroso). It was undoubtedly a dedication to Kephisos. A charming fresh work of the 3rd century B. C. The portrayal of the figure is flat, with only one principal view, but the view of the column is slanting. Clearly it represents a mythological person (according to one opinion Ianiskos of the household of Asklepios). Height 0.86 m., width of the plinth 0.36 m. (Pl. 63).

1462. Simple relief. Herakles, stretched out on the ground to the left, on his lionskin, enjoys the shade of a tree, where hang his club and his quiver. In front of him, below, his food. In his left hand he holds a flat cup (with wine). On the right, at the back, standing, a small Satyr (with antithetic motion) plays the double flute. A work full of life with Hellenistic intoxication and with the beginning of centrifugal movement, influenced by a painted prototype. Probably of the end the 3rd century B.C. Found at Eleusis in 1888. Height 0.39 m., width 0.40 m.

1453. Votive relief with horizontal cornice. Kore (Persephone), seated on a round base, holds in her left hand a large torch and offers her (right) hand to the standing Demeter who is covered to the top of her polos with her himation. On the head of the Kore are two ears of wheat (?). On the right a man standing, short (for this reason more probably a mortal rather than Pluto), offers libations with a phiale and holds a sceptre or staff. Between him and Kore is Cerberus, with two heads. On the left a small girl standing holds a sheaf which may be a broom (as in the *Ion* of Euripides). Above her a small winged figure is flying with a wreath in her hand. According to the inscription the small girl is Agathokleia whose father dedicated her to Demeter and Kore (to become a young priestess ?). Found at Gytheion, known since 1873. Worthy of note, though a mediocre work, for its echoes of the style of the 2nd century B. C. (the antithetic turning of the girl, the representation of Cerberus slanting toward the centre, etc.). The old interpretation of the seated goddess as Demeter is proved wrong by the type of the veiled standing goddess which is known from representations of Demeter of the 4th century B.C. Height 0.46 m., width 0.56 m.

1659. Statue of a woman, headless, with round plinth. The slender body rests on the left leg; the himation passes diagonally in front of the breast; the left arm, fastened to the body, restrains the himation. A grave statue or — more probably — a statue of Persephone who held a torch in her right hand. It has the slenderness of the end of the 4th century B.C. or the beginning of the 3rd, influenced by Praxitelean creations. Found at Karystos. Height 1.53 m. (with the plinth of which the height is 0.07 m.).

2237. Head of a god (from an Hermaic stele ?), bearded. Band around the hair which leaves free the delicate ears and falls in waves behind the neck. Good archaïstic work of the Hellenistic period. Found at Eretria in 1891. See the following. Height 0.26 m.

2814. Head of a young man, flat above. It lacks part of the skull, originally a separate piece of marble. A work well delineated but cold, of the advanced Hellenistic period or provincial of the 4th century B.C. Found at Eretria. See also the adjacent nos. 2237 and 383. Height 0.16 m.

383. Head of Silenos from poros, in front of a building block and joined with it. The mouth open, the thick moustache falls downward. Of the 4th century or the Hellenistic period. Found at Eretria at 1889, it would perhaps have been built into the gate in the wall near the theatre. Height 0.40 m., width 0.35 m., depth 0.32 - 0.33 m.

232. Statue of Aristonoe, priestess of Nemesis, with its plinth, wedged into a square base. According to the in-

scription carved on the latter it was dedicated by Hierokles
the son of Aristonoe to Themis and Nemesis. She stands on
her right leg and turns her face to the same side. The folds of
the himation which fall at the side of the relaxed leg have life
and naturalness. At the back, however, the surface of the
body is flat. Provincial but not arid, a work with the beginning of centrifugal movement. End of the 3rd or early 2nd
century B.C. Found at Rhamnous in Attica in 1890, inside
the temple of the goddess. It is not certain whether the arm
(by the wall) belongs. Height 1.62 m.

3556. Bust of a young man, beardless, once inserted in
a portrait statue. Diadem around the head, the hair (unworked behind) covers the neck. Marked turning upward and
toward the left shoulder, the glance somewhat dim. It probably represented the Anatolian philhellene Ariarathes the fifth,
King of Cappadocia. An Attic work of about 120 B.C. with
tender carving of the face, it shows the heroization of the
subject after death. Found in the excavations of the west slopes
of the Acropolis in 1887. The statue would perhaps have stood
in the agora of Athens. Against the identification with Ariarathes the ninth or with another leader of the beginning
of the first century B. C. the chief argument is the antithetic movement of the head in relation to the right shoulder; this suggests an earlier date. Height 0.40 m.

1318. Grave stele of Miltiades. The relief, with concave
background, is crowned by an arch resting on pilasters. On
the right the deceased, standing, rests his hand on a Hermaic stele; on the left a slave. Below, the inscription : «*Miltiades Diodorou. Hail, good and happy one*». Beginning of the
first century B.C. Found on Rheneia. Height to the summit
of the arch 0.65 m.

1661. Grave statue of a Harpy, female figure, winged,
with an irregular base. She has heavy legs and arms, hoofs of

an animal, and rests with her right elbow on a funeral vase above a carved base. An unfinished work, almost coarse, though characteristic of the period are the sense of depth and the centrifugal movement (breast toward the interior and the left, the head with inclination toward the right). Found on Rheneia, before 1830; of the 2nd century B.C. Total height 0.68 m., height of the figure 0.77 m., width of the base below 0.69 m.

1317. Grave stele in the form of a shrine with pediment. Doorposts with Corinthian capitals, epistyle, triglyphs, metopes with bucrania in relief, thorax and helmet (?). Three figures with portrait characteristics. Below in three lines traces of the names, the lower section on the left missing. Found on Rheneia before 1830. Representative work of island grave sculpture in Hellenistic times. End of the 2nd century B.C. Height 0.83 m. (with the restoration of the pediment).

3688. Statue of a man, headless, with its round plinth. He stands on his left leg, which is advanced, bent. The himation, hanging low, gives a serious appearance to the excellent, slender - bodied work. Probably of the end of the Hellenistic period, reflection of some good original. Found in 1930 in Athens (Varvakeion). Height 0.47 m.

1194. Grave stele in the form of a shrine with cornice, pediment and Corinthian columns. Three deceased persons are portrayed from the family of Apollonios : on the left Mysta, seated, facing right, on a high stool, with footstool; on the right, standing, two men; on the edges a small maid servant and a slave. Below the figures, on a concave surface, the names are carved in three columns in a perpendicular arrangement. Found on Rheneia, it is one of the good island stelai of the 2nd century B.C. Height 1.23 m., width below 0.83 m.

3248. Statue of Aphrodite, headless, with a round plinth.

She steps with the left foot on a bird (swan or goose). The left leg, relaxed, has an inclination toward the centre; the breast forward, bare above the himation. Late Hellenistic remodelling of a Pheidian work, a transition from the centrifugal formation of the 2nd century to the flat 'modelling of the 1st century B.C. Found at Argos in 1878. Height 0.70 m., height of the plinth 0.05 m.

2585. Small votive statue of Aphrodite, headless.She is dressed in a diaphanous chiton, girded high, the himation covers her lower body only, below the buttocks. The left leg advances with emphasis.. The upper body has a snake - like turn, the left shoulder is raised. An elegant Attic work combined with the centrifugal movement of the ripe Hellenistic style. 2nd half of the 2nd century B.C. Found in 1904 near the Theseion. Height 0.64 m.

235. Colossal statue of Poseidon with its square plinth. He stands on the right foot, the other is drawn back noticeably. Inclination of the head toward the right. With his lowered left hand he presses firmly to his hips the himation which covers the hand below. In the raised right hand he would have held his trident. A large dolphin, fastened perpendicularly to his right thigh serves as support. Work of the advanced Hellenistic period (end of the centrifugal or « open » form), provincial, influenced by prototypes from Asia Minor, it portrays by superficial emphasis a princely status devoid of true divinity. Found in 1877 on Melos, with the statues nos. 236 and 238. Height 2.17 m. The old plaster restorations to the head have been removed (P l. 66).

3463. Head of a young man with the neck, once inserted in a statue. The diadem around his head, its inclination upwards and toward the left shoulder, and the expression suggest that Alexander the Great is represented. A diagonal cutting of the skull for the attachment of another

piece of marble. Good workmanship of the Hellenistic period
(apparent especially in the locks of hair). Provenance
unknown. In the National Museum since 1920. Height 0.34 m.

1158. Small grave stele of a girl, Phila, with pediment.
Found at Tarsus in Cilicia. 2nd century B.C. Height 0.57 m.,
width 0.32 m.

3485. The « little refugee ». Small statue of a child,
with an unusual plinth. Still a baby he can scarcely stand
on his feet. He wears a thick hood and holds a dog in his
two hands in front of him. The support at the side for the left
leg and the inferior quality of the work favour a date in the
1st century A.D. The original, however, would have been
a graceful little work most probably of the 3rd century B.C.
Found in 1922 in the Gerontikon of Nyssa (Asia Minor) and
brought to the Museum by the finder K. Kourouniotes in
the first days of the Smyrna disaster (August 1922). Height
of the plinth 0.69 m., height of the little statue 0.63 m.
(Pl. 67).

1154. Grave stele with pediment and acroterion. In the centre, within a hollow square, the relief: on the right a woman
is seated on a stool facing left. In front of her a small maidser-
vant with a fan; standing opposite, a young man, his body
frontal, gazes calmly toward the woman. The bare surface
above and below sets off the relief. Provenance unknown.
One of the good stelai of the period, with excellent preservation. End of the 2nd century B.C. Height 1.33 m., width
below 0.565 m.

362-363. Two portrait heads, man and wife, from a
grave monument. Found in Smyrna in 1884. Good, noble
works of the late Hellenistic period (about 100 B.C), showing the disembodiment of death; they have a classicistic
reversion. No 362 : height 0.44 m.; no. 363 : height 0.455 m.

1156. Grave stele of a young woman with pediment. The relief within a square metopic hollow. A young lady, Lampron, frontal, with chiton and diaphanous himation which covers the head, is represented heroized like a statue, in the pose of a known work of that period. On the left a maid servant with long girded peplos holds the pyxis and in her right hand a fan. Above, a band encircles the stele in low relief, formerly coloured red. Below the inscription : « *Lampron Stymphalia, good wife of Sarapion, greeting* ». The delicate, mournful face is enhanced by sensitive carving. Splendid preservation. Found on Rheneia. One of the best island stelai of the period, about 120 B.C. Total height 1.45 m.

351. Portrait head from a statue of a foreign priest. Beardless, he wears around his head a thick foliate wreath. Tufted locks of hair cover his temples, others abundantly shown fall on his neck, leaving his ears free. The small eyes and the heavily accented brow - ridge suggest a type, probably Thracian. Excellent Attic work of an important sculptor of the beginning of the 1st century B.C.; brilliant, pitiless rendering of the dry flesh of the face. Found in Athens in 1837. Height 0.31 m.

1485. Votive stele with horizontal cornice. Low relief in three successive zones. On the right seated, frontal, Cybele with high polos, holds in her left hand the drum, in her lowered right hand the phiale. Below, her lion. In the centre, standing, Apollo Kitharodos offers a libation with his right hand above an altar, toward which a small attendant leads a lamb. Behind, on the left, a flute player and a woman. A tree is sketched behind the altar. In the lower narrow zones, banqueters, and, lower, servants with kraters, etc. On the left, a dancing girl and a flute player. The left frame has been vertically broken. According to the inscription below, a guild, men and women, crown the priestess of Apollo and Cybele

(119 B.C.). Found at Nikaia in Bithynia. Known from an old drawing of Ghyzis (about 1865) as is the following, no. 1486. Height 0.83 m., width below 0.395 m. See also the adjacent no. 1486.

1486. Votive stele of a type similar to the previous no. 1485. In the hollow square, a low relief : on the right Apollo with sceptre offers libation upon an altar to which a small acolyte is leading a sheep. Farther to the left a young girl with a large basket on her head holds an oinochoe, beside her the donor « worships ». On a branch of a high tree behind the altar sits a crow. Below, the inscription of the guild who crown Asklepiades son of Melidoros, who had held a priesthood. Found at Nikaia in Bithynia. End of the Hellenistic period. Height 0.81 m., maximum width 0.475 m.

1632. Composition, half finished, of two frontal figures. On the left a bearded man, standing, with long himation, embraces with his left hand a woman (with short neck). Her left breast is bared. The arrangement is in one plane, without any spatial development of the figures. (Dionysos and a Maenad ?) Provenance unknown. Height 0.62 m., width 0.29 m.

2877. Statue of Artemis, headless. She wears a light peplos, girded high, with a long overfold. From the left arm hangs her himation. She runs forward impetuously, with right leg forward, the folds of her chiton windblown. A fresh Hellenistic minor work influenced by an important contemporary work of art. Middle of the 2nd century B.C. Found in Akarnania. Height 0.21 m.

Br. 14612. Bronze portrait head of a mature fleshy man, beardless. He has an inclination toward the left shoulder, his glance directed slightly upward and outward. His jowls heavy, his face wrinkled. The confusion of planes customary in older works has become calm, the weary expression shows a secret pathos. It belonged to a statue of a Greek more probably than to that of a Roman (according to the most recent technological research). One of the best portraits of the late Hellenistic period, about 100 B.C. The head was cast separately from the body. Found on Delos in 1912. Height 0.325 m.

429. Large bust of a beardless young man, once inserted in a statue. The flat diadem around the rich hair, the inclination toward the left, and the upward glance, influenced by statues of Alexander the Great, suggest a Hellenistic ruler. Found on Delos in 1884 together with no. 552. The surface eaten by salt. 2nd century B.C. Height 0.55 m.

552. Head of a mature woman, of over life size, with part of the neck, once inserted in a portrait statue. It has antithetic inclination toward the left shoulder; at the back a piece of marble formerly attached, is missing. Band around the head to show kingly or princely character. The surface of the face much worn away by salt. Found on Delos in 1884 with no. 429. 2nd century B.C. Height 0.45 m.

1751-55. Five theatrical masks of marble. Three are in high relief in front of a heavy plaque, originally coloured. All represent types of the New Comedy. They were found west of the stoa of Attalos about 1898 : they would have been built into some building of the ancient Agora (the theatre of Agrippa ?). Probably of the 1st century B.C. Width of the plaque 0.46 m., depth 0.10 m.

221-222. Two parts of a small frieze with relief figures : Tritons and Nereids, Cupids who ride on sea animals. Below, the sea is shown by wavy lines (formerly coloured blue). Found at Molos near Lamia. Carving somewhat arid, of the late Hellenstic period (1st century B.C.) The subject copies a fresh earlier prototype. No. 221 : length 1.60 m.; no. 222 : length 0.48 m., height 0.17 m.

1829. Statue of Artemis. The goddess, dressed in chiton and with peplos (the overfold girded), moves forward advancing the right leg which is bent. The pleated edge of the himation falls from below the left arm, separating the two legs. The head, small and narrow, is crowned with a plait. The lower part of the arms missing. Found on Delos in the House of the Diadoumenos. Hellenistic adaptation of an original of the end of the 4th century B.C. Height 1.40 m. Height of the head with the slender neck 0.26 - 0.27 m.

4546. Statue of Serapis, with the plinth attached to a square base. He wears a short, sleeved chiton and short himation. The head, turned toward the side of the left leg which is relaxed, introduces a feeling of openness into the movement. The statue has the spectacular pose of the colossal Poseidon of Melos (no. 235). On the base the inscription : *Timokles Timokleidous Sarapidi*. Found in 1954 on Amorgos. About 100 B.C. Height 0.52 m., width of the base 0.565 m.

3335. Statue of Aphrodite and Pan, with plinth inserted in a flat, square base. The goddess, nude, with her weight on her right leg, raises her sandal in her right ·hand threateningly against goat-footed Pan (who possibly surprises her in her bath). Over her shoulder flies a small smiling Cupid who grasps the horn of Pan. The binding of the hair ingenious. About 100 B.C. Found in 1904 on Delos, in the house of the Poseidoniastai of Beirut. The technique cold and faultless. The waxpolishing on the face and the body gives a certain warmth to the white surface. Classisistic, the sculptor's modification lies in the composition which is arranged for one particular view (there is only a slight inclination of the upper body inwards). The Hellenistic original which had a developed sense of depth and a cool humour is echoed by the adjacent bronze statue (No. **Br. 7406**. Height 0.24 m., from Athens). The body of Aphrodite is bent back, the legs together, the movement of the body antithetic. Height of Aphrodite 1.29

m., of Pan 1.17 m. Height of the base 0.125 m., width of the base 0.55 m., depth 1.315 m. (Pl. 68).

322. Bust of a woman, once inserted in a grave statue. The himation covers the head as well. Parts of the head which were once made from a separate piece of marble are missing. Inferior, but not unexpressive work, more probably of the 1st century A.D. Found on Amorgos in 1888. Height 0.31 m., width below 0.31 m.

780. The upper part of a grave statue of a woman. The light himation covers the head as well. Replica of a known type. The carving of the himation shows great care; the expression of the face vacant. About 100 B.C. Found on Thera. Height 0.84 m., width below 0.45 m.

438. Bust of Serapis, once inserted in a statue (perhaps seated). The thick locks of hair fall to the shoulders. Careful carving, dry, of the 1st century B.C., after a work of the 4th century of the sculptor Bryaxis. From Asia Minor. Height 0.26 m., width of the shoulders 0.28 m.

3377. Colossal head of Zeus, once inserted in a large seated statue. Betow the fleshy eyebrows, deep - set eyes, now empty but originally inset with other materials. The mouth half open. The hair, which leaves the ears free, was supplemented on top with other pieces of marble. A metal crown would have encircled the head. The mass of the beard, which is divided in the middle into repeated locks of wavy hair almost windblown, shows up, by contrast, the surface - skin of the face, which is carved with care and with an inherited sensitiveness to variation in the planes. From a single piece of Pentelic marble, the whole head has a hollow at the back, necessary to facilitate transport. Large holes serve for the ǝʍdging ofthe back part of the head. Found at Aegeira in Achaia in 1916. It belongs to a large seated cult - statue which Pausanias saw, a work of the Athenian sculptor Eukleides.

The head has the plastic shaping and, in its expression, the
meticulous care of the advanced Hellenistic period (2nd century B.C.). Thestatue was without doubt one of the best contemporary works of its kind. Height 0.87 m., width 0.50 m.
(Pl. 69).

3481. The left arm of the statue of Zeus. It is slightly bent.
In the fingers are preserved traces of the sceptre. The plastic
shaping on a grand scale, summary. Found in 1920 at Aegeira. Width 1.33 m. **3481 a.** (By the wall). A finger from the
right hand of Zeus. Found in 1925. Width 0.11 m.

236. Statue of a woman, of overlife size, with its thick,
rounded plinth. The inserted head is missing. The arms as
well as part of the breast were made from a separate piece of
marble and inserted. The peplos, not totally diaphanous, has
folds which thicken between and around the feet. The relaxed
(left) leg is noticeably conceived from the side. Mediocre
work, its casual execution is evident especially in the rendering of the himation wrapped around the front of the abdomen. Found on Melos in 1877, together with the Poseidon;
it would have represented Amphitrite. The original, richer at
least in its movement and in the folds, would have belonged
to an Asia Minor school of sculpture. Height 0.92 m.

457. Head of a youth, his hair completely covered with
bands. It belonged to a portrait statue. It has only a very
slight turning toward the left shoulder and evidently the
intention was to idealize and beautify. The marble is not without life. Attic work of the 2nd half of the 1st century B.C.,
transitional from late Hellenistic to classicistic art. Found in
Athens (Stoa of Attalos) about 1860. Height 0.23 m.

259 - 260. Two plaques with two women dancers in relief
(Hores ?). The first, no. 259, steps with calm rhythm toward
the left, covered to the neck in her himation, her body clearly
sketched on the marble. The second, no. 260, wrapped to

the top of her head in a himation of many folds, dances on her toes toward the left, while with an expression of emotion she bends her beautiful face. Of metallic character is the linear hardness of the folds, though with accurate carving. Soulless work, intellectual, but also romantic from a Neo-Attic workshop of the end of the 1st century B.C.; no. 260 echoes monuments of the 4th century B.C.; No. 259 seems to be an eclectic Neo-Attic creation. The hollowing of the plaques from the front suggests the hypothesis that, together with a third which is not preserved, they would have formed the base of a bronze tripod. Found in .1862 in the theatre of Dionysos. Height of no. 259 : 1.07 m., width 0.66 m.; height of no. 260 : 1.01 m., width 0.64 m. See also (particularly for the toe - stepping of the dancer) the adjacent no. **2667**, badly preserved, with flat surface. This was probably also found in the same place as the two previous, but from another monument. Height 0.95 m., width 0.62 m.

563. Head of a young woman. The pictorial accuracy in the rendering of the locks of hair and the attempt at nobility of expression show a romantic influence from works of the 5th century B.C. Attic work of the 2nd half of the 1st century B.C. Found in the Kerameikos, it would have belonged to a grave statue. Height 0.29 m.

255. Statue of Dionysos dressed in a himation. The locks of hair fall on his shoulders. Inferior, empty work of the late Hellenistic period, probably in the 2nd half of the 2nd century B.C. Found at Eleusis in 1885. Height 1.15 m.

4547. Large head of a god, with the neck, once inserted in a (cult ?) statue. It is of the type of the statues of Zeus of the classical period. The hair falls richly, covering the ears also; the small mouth half open. Under the weathered surface of the face the movement of the planes can be discerned. It is, however, uncertain whether this mediocre wrok should be dated to the Hellenistic or to the Roman period. Provenance unknown. Height 0.97 m.

238. Statue of a goddess, headless, with its plinth. Over the chiton she wears a short diaphanous himation which covers the whole of her right arm. She stands with left leg crossed and is supported by her left elbow on the high polos of a statue of a young woman (Aphrodite ?) of archaistic type, standing on a rock. A work far from arid of the final Hellenistic period, influenced by a good original. Found in 1877 on Melos together with the nearby no. 236 and with the large Poseidon. End of the 2nd century B.C. Height 1.10 m.

CORRIGENDA

No. 22 (p. 9)
  for «which appears» read «bent forward,»

No. 2891 (p. 12)
  insert *«cp the»* before «adjacent»

No. 29 (p. 17)
  for «to the edge» read «on the ledge»

No. 3370 (p. 23)
  for «undeveloped» read «developed»

No. 3938 (p. 28)
  for «advancing» read «advanced»

No. 740 (p. 35)
  for «planes» read «folds»

p. 46 for «its form, the shrine» read «form into the shrine»

p. 47 for **713** read **711**

No. 1419 (p. 57)
  for « *carved* (it) » read *«was secretary»*

No. 274 (p. 65)
for «Above the helmet a　read　« On the helmet, on either side,
Sphinx, with the figure　　　　a Sphinx; in ·the middle a fi-
of Pegasos».　　　　　　　　　gure of Pegasos».

No. 129 (p. 69)
for «analogies»　　　　read　«characteristic features»

No. 723 (p. 82)
for «400 B. C.»　　　　read　«360 B. C.»

No. 1826 (p. 86)
for «the bent leg»　　　read　«the tensed leg»

No. 1597 (p. 97)
for «Eros touches her　read　«Eros stands lightly on the
lightly with the palm of　　　palm of her left hand».
his left hand».

No. 257 (p. 98)
for «who holds a tragic　read　«who holds a tragic mask above
mask of Silenus above　　　　the right shoulder of Silenus.»
the right shoulder».

No. 146 (p. 102)
for «above a small person　read　«on her right thigh which»
on the right who»

No. 3716 (p. 119)
for «her breast at the top»　read　«her torso spreading over the
upper half»

No. 825 (p. 120)
for «the Museum of　read　«in the Berlin Museum are
Berlin; the head is also　　　preserved two servant girls,
preserved.»　　　　　　　　　with heads intact»

No. 820 (p. 125)
for «leaning slightly on　read　«supporting her lightly by the
her hand»　　　　　　　　　　arm»

No. 4464 (p. 127)
for « rendering »　　　read　« tradition »

PLATES

PLATE 1

Statue of a seated Goddess (No 57)

PLATE 2

a. Grave monument of Kitylos and Dermys (No 56),
b. Archaic Metope from Mycenae (No 2869)

PLATE 3

The " Dipylon Head " (No 3372)

PLATE 4

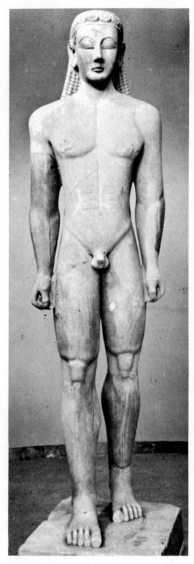

The " Sounion Kouros " (No 2720)

PLATE 5

The " Kouros from Melos "   (No 1558)

PLATE 6

Statue of Winged Victory, from Delos (No 21)

PLATE 7

The " Dipylon Diskophoros " (No 38)

PLATE 8

Grave stele of Aristion, work of Aristokles (No 29)

PLATE 9

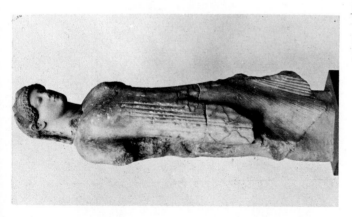

a-b. Two Statues of Korai (Nos 24 and 26)

PLATE 10

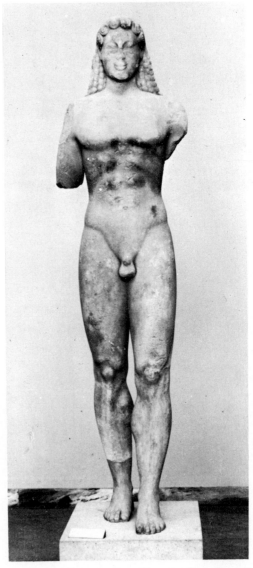

The " Kouros from Kea " (No 3686)

PLATE 11

Mask of Dionysos from Dionyso in Attica (No 3072),
Sculpture from the pediment of an archaic temple (No 1673). (The left half in New York)

PLATE 12

The " Stele of the Running Hoplite " (No 1959)

PLATE 13

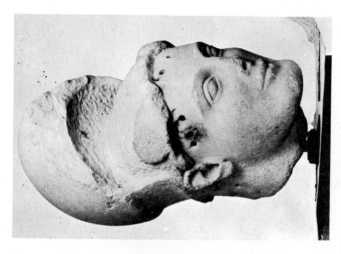

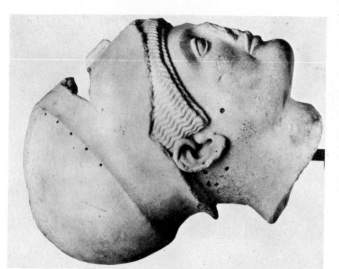

a - b. Two Heads from the Temple of Aphaia on Aegina (No 1933 - 34)

PLATE 14

Kouros from the Ilissos (No 3687)

PLATE 15

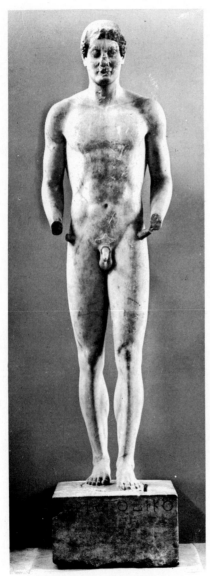

Aristodikos (No 3938)

PLATE 16

a - b. Two Reliefs from the square base of a Kouros (No 3476)

PLATE 17

The " Disk of Melos " (No 3990)

PLATE 18

The "Selfcrowned". Votive Relief from Sounion (No 3344)

PLATE 19

Grave stele of Amphotto (No 739)

PLATE 20

The " Large Relief from Eleusis " (No 126)

PLATE 21

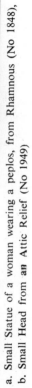

a. Small Statue of a woman wearing a peplos, from Rhamnous (No 1848),
b. Small Head from an Attic Relief (No 1949)

PLATE 22

Statue of Hebe (?), Akroterion from an Athenian temple (No 1732)

PLATE 23

The " Poseidon from Artemision " (No br. 15161)

PLATE 24

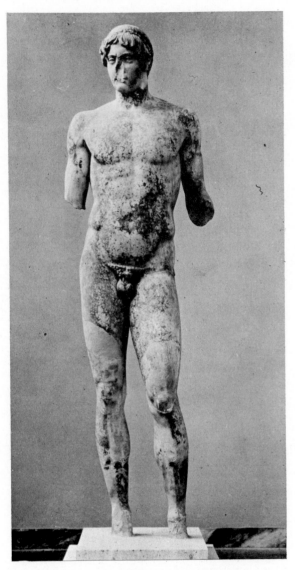

The " Omphalos Apollo " (No 45)

PLATE 25

Grave stele of a Youth (No 715)

PLATE 26

a - b. Kore (Persephone) from Piraeus (No 176)

PLATE 27

Relief of Echelos and Basile (No 1783)

PLATE 28

a. Head of a Goddess from the Argive Heraion (No 1571),
b. Plaque from the sima of the Argive Heraion (No 3973)

PLATE 29

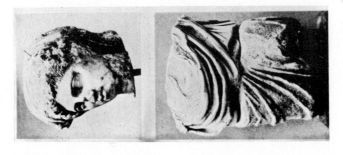

a. Parts of a Statue from Rhamnous (Nos 203, 208),
b. Part of a Relief from a Decree (No 1419)

PLATE 30

Stele of Diotima from Mantineia (No 226)

PLATE 31

The " Varvakeion Athena " (No 129)

PLATE 32

Grave stele of Hegeso (No 3624)

PLATE 33

a. Grave stele of Polyxena (No 723),
b. Statue of a woman from Delos (No 1827)

PLATE 34

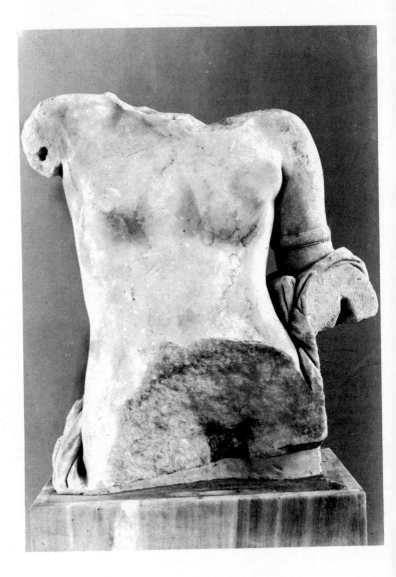

Torso of a Statue of Aphrodite (No 227)

PLATE 35

Relief from Lerna (No 3617)

PLATE 36

Relief of Telephanes from Pentelicon (No 4465)

PLATE 37

Akroterion from the Temple of Asklepios at Epidauros (No 157)

PLATE 38

Statue of Hygeia from Epidauros (No 299)

PLATE 39

The " Stele from the Ilissos " (No 869)

PLATE 40

a. The " Stele of the Farewell " (No 870),
b. Grave stele of a Woman (No 3716)

PLATE 41

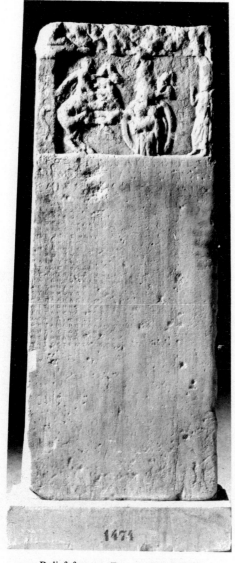

Relief from a Decree (No 1474)

PLATE 42

a. Votive Relief from Piraeus (No 1403),
b. The " Relief of the Charioteer " (No 1341)

PLATE 43

Statue of a Little Girl (No 693)

PLATE 44

The " Asklepios from Munychia " (No 258)

PLATE 45

a. Votive Relief to Asklepios (No 1332),
b. Votive Relief to Asklepios from Kynouria (No 1402)

PLATE 46

Relief with the Recognition of Odysseus (No 1914)

PLATE 47

a. Votive Relief to Amphiaraos (No 3369),
b. Votive Relief to a " Hero Doctor " (No 3526)

PLATE 48

Offering to the Nymphs, from Eleusis (No 1445)

PLATE 49

Horse from a large Stele (No 4464)

PLATE 50

a - b. Two Plaques from Funeral Shrines (Nos 4496, 1283)

PLATE 51

a - b. Two Reliefs from the Base of a Tripod (No 1463)

PLATE 52

Youth from Antikythera (No br. 13396)

PLATE 53

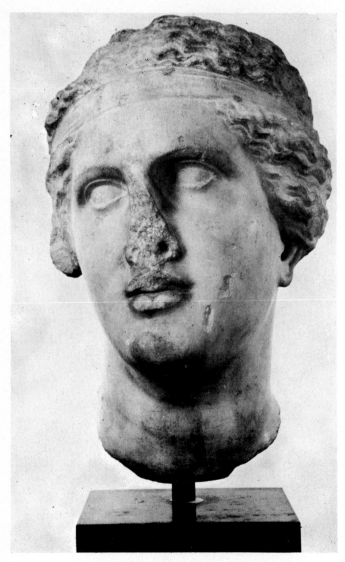

Head of Ariadne (No 182)

PLATE 54

Head of Hygeia (No 3602)

PLATE 55

Head of a Statue of Athena (No 3004)

PLATE 56

Statue of Themis from Rhamnous (No 231)

PLATE 57

Colossal Head of Demeter from Lykosoura (No 1734)

PLATE 58

a - b. Triton (female) from the Throne from Lykosoura (No 2171)

PLATE 59

The " Eubouleus " from Eleusis (No 181)

PLATE 60

The " Satyr from Lamia ", akroterion from an unknown temple (No 239)

PLATE 61

Bronze Head from a Statue of a Philosopher (No br. 13400)

PLATE 62

Grave stele from Tenos (No 1028)

PLATE 63

Statue of a Boy from Lilaia of Parnassos (No 2772)

PLATE 64

Fragment of a small votive Relief (No 2811)

PLATE 65

Grave Statue of a Woman from Rheneia (No 380)

PLATE 66

The " Poseidon from Melos " (No 235)

PLATE 67

The " Little Refugee ". Statuette of a Boy from Asia Minor (No 3485)

PLATE 68

Group of Aphrodite, Pan, and Eros, from Delos (No 3335)

PLATE 69

Colossal Head of Zeus from Aigeira (No 3377)

THIS BRIEF GUIDE OF THE ARCH-
AEOLOGICAL MUSEUM — B' SCUL-
PTURE — IS PUBLISHED IN THE SE-
RIES OF THE ARCHAEOLOGICAL
GUIDES — NO. 15 — OF THE GENE-
RAL DIRECTION OF ANTIQUITIES
AND RESTORATION IN AUGUST
1967. PRINTED IN ATHENS BY CHAR.
SYNODINOS, LEKKA 7 (TEXT) AND
JOHN MAKRIS, GRAPHIC ARTS, 34
KIFISSIAS STR. (PLATES AND CO-
VER). SUPERVISED BY ATHENA KA-
LOGEROPOULOU. PLATES ARRAN-
GED BY A. XYNGOPOULOS.